Donated by

Warren Kump M.D.

© DEMCO, INC. 1990 PRINTED IN U.S.A.

CONDITION CRITICAL:
OUR HOSPITAL CRISIS

Other books by Edwin P. Hoyt

Jumbos and Jackasses
The Vanderbilts
    and Their Fortunes
The Supersalesmen
The Tempering Years
Spectacular Rogue
A Gentleman of Broadway
The Golden Rot
Marilyn
    (A BIOGRAPHY OF MARILYN MONROE)
The House of Morgan
A Matter of Conscience
    (A NOVEL)
The Last Cruise of the Emden

Edwin P. Hoyt

CONDITION
CRITICAL

Our Hospital Crisis

HOLT, RINEHART AND WINSTON
New York   Chicago   San Francisco

Designer: Ernst Reichl
83765-0116
Printed in the United States of America

For Helga Hoyt in the hope that
if she ever really does practice medicine
matters will have changed somewhat
for the better.

CONTENTS

CONDITION CRITICAL:
OUR HOSPITAL CRISIS

Chapter One

AMERICAN
HOSPITALS

In the summer of 1965, on the occasion of the passage of the Medicare law to provide low-cost medical and hospital care for all of America's aged who want it, a survey of America's hospitals and health programs indicated such serious deficiencies as to threaten the national health.

While United States hospitals housed 1,700,000 beds, only 700,000 of these were readily available to general hospital patients. Many of these beds were in obsolete or overcrowded buildings. The 1,000,000 beds occupied by long-term or chronic patients did not come near meeting the need, for in the field of mental health alone there was a shortage that authorities placed at around 450,000 beds.

Other statistics were equally alarming:

Of some 500,000 beds in nursing or convalescent homes, 193,000 were considered definitely substandard, and there was need for another 300,000 nursing-home beds. The need was especially serious in 1966 because, with the beginning of hospital admissions under the Medicare pro-

gram in July, every person over 65 who registered for
Medicare would be eligible for insured stays in convalescent or nursing homes, and in order to meet the needs of
the American people the nursing-home beds would have
to be fully used.

The shortages in personnel were more than vexing.
Some 600,000 registered nurses were working full time
in 1965 and another 70,000 were working part time, yet
there were shortages nearly everywhere, particularly in
rural areas. It was estimated that by 1970 an additional
300,000 nurses would be needed. How were they going
to be supplied?

Where, for that matter, were the needed doctors and
other health workers going to come from? The World
Health Organization's most recent report (1963) showed a
total of 242,000 physicians in the United States, a ratio of
1 to each 710 people, and forecast that by 1975 the nation
must be graduating 11,000 doctors a year, instead of 7,500,
just to keep up with the growth of population. This would
mean the creation of 20 to 24 new medical schools.

The same problem existed on every level in the health
occupations. More nursing schools were needed to graduate more nurses. The 68,000 medical technicians in America in 1965 represented about three-quarters of the immediate need. There were serious shortages of X-ray
technicians, practical nurses, and other specialists.

Americans had long been told that their system of health
care was the best in the world. Suddenly—it seemed—doctors, hospital administrators, and public officials began
saying that unless drastic steps were taken to improve the
nation's health program, Americans would soon fall behind other countries.

The fact is, however, that the United States had long

been behind the advanced nations of Western Europe in hospitalization, and behind many countries, including the Soviet Union, in the ratio of physicians to the population at large. In 1963 the United States had one doctor to every 710 persons, while the Soviet Union had one doctor to every 529 persons.

In terms of hospitalization, at least fifteen other nations could show higher ratios of hospital beds available to the population than the 9.1-per-thousand that existed in the United States.[1]

Generally speaking, too, this figure followed very closely the pattern of two other sets of statistics that are important indicators in the matter of national health: national death rate and infant mortality rate. In both, the United States was far down the list in the 1960's, well below the leaders of Western Europe.

In national death rates reported to the World Health Organization in 1963, eight European countries showed fewer deaths per thousand than the United States.[2]

In infant mortality, the United States was in no better place than tenth among the nations of the world.[3]

To be sure, the American position was not desperate in comparison with those of the less developed countries of the world. Health figures were not even available in 1965 for most of the new African nations. In the Philippines, where the United States has long had interests and influence, infant mortality occurred at the rate of 73 per thousand births. In the Philippines, of course, there was only one doctor for every 7,000 inhabitants, compared to ten times that number in the United States, and the Philippines could claim only one hospital bed for every five thousand people. Comparisons with the underdeveloped countries could not possibly be meaningful; the American health problem in the 1960's was to maintain and increase a healthful environment for its people, in an urbanized and industrialized society, using all the conveniences of a modern technology.

How well were the people of the United States actually faring? The figures and facts showed they were not faring nearly so well as they had been led to believe.

If, quantitatively, the world health figures showed the United States definitely trailing the leaders in matters of hospitalization and health services, it must be recalled that all those leaders enjoyed some form of government subsidy or support, ranging from the developing social insurance policies of Canada to the government-operated National Health Service of Great Britain. In the Medicare law of 1965 the United States was just beginning to find its way in a field where other nations had pioneered a decade and more before.[4] In the four years 1957-1960, Canada increased its governmental expenditures for health services from $32 per person to $52 per person, while the United States government in 1960 spent only $30 per person.

Qualitatively, Americans also had very little to boast about in 1965. Changes in the population and in the structure of American society in the twentieth century had scarcely begun to be reflected in the hospitalization program of the nation at large. Often the rapid shift of population created chaos. In many regions of expanding population there were serious shortages of hospital beds, while in areas deserted by this population the hospitals suffered from lack of patronage. Yet this latter could be only a temporary problem, because the increased emphasis on hospitalization brought about by Medicare would soon mean the straining of every hospital facility in the land.

In 1965 too many of those facilities were already badly strained in several ways.

Although hospital personnel and expenses had steadily increased, and many advances in medical technique had been made since the end of World War II, the overall standard of health treatment in America had actually declined. Dr. Alonzo S. Yerby, New York City's Hospital Commissioner in 1965, told the White House Conference on Health in November of that year that basic medical facilities for America's poor were "crowded, uncomfortable, and lacking in concern for human dignity." They were regressing toward those of the old hospital dispensaries of two centuries earlier.

In other countries of the world, efforts were being made to improve the position of the poor in matters of health. Denmark had strengthened its health-insurance program to make it virtually all-inclusive in 1961. Finland had drawn plans for national health insurance. France was coordinating its social security and increasing the benefits. West Germany was unifying its sickness-insurance schemes and expanding them. All this while, Dr. Yerby said, the American poor were being forced into hospital emergency rooms and out-patient departments that resembled the primitive dispensaries, except that they were not even free of charge.

The skyrocketing of expense was part of the problem of American health care. In 1965 American hospital expenses totalled more than $12 billion, with nearly $8 billion of that amount spent for wages and payments to personnel. In the years since World War II neither the number of hospitals nor the number of beds had risen anything like the cost, in proportion. The number of people employed in hospitals had nearly doubled. This should have meant, then, that hospital care in the United States was vastly improved over 1948.[5]

But was it?

One of the most serious problems of American hospitals in the 1960's was the lag in enforcing the practice of up-to-date medicine. A survey conducted under the auspices of the Columbia University School of Public Health in 1964 indicated that the chances of a paying patient achieving the best health care in a New York City hospital that year were no better than one in two. What was wrong? As one medical educator put it, the medicine practiced in American hospitals in 1965 was too often the medicine of 1940—and this after a quarter of a century in which advances in medicine had tumbled upon one another so rapidly that the progress was as great as that of the 100 previous years.

And it could not be said that New York City did not have excellent hospitals. Quite to the contrary, several of the most advanced hospitals in the nation—Columbia Presbyterian Medical Center, New York Hospital, Mount Sinai—gave the best possible hospital service; but, New York was also the home of some outmoded, understaffed hospitals where care could by no means be called good. New York City was no exception, but a magnified example of the problem of the nation at large.

The most serious of all hospital problems in the United States, and one that could not readily be solved by enterprise and education, was the problem of cost. The $12 billion spent in 1965 showed how hospital costs had soared each year to new and dizzier heights, at the rate, over a ten-year period, of about ten percent per year. In 1965 and 1966 hospital boards and administrators struggled with rising costs that forced some of them to deficits

and others to invade their capital endowment.[6] Higher
costs were passed on to patients. What could be done?
John M. Danielson, President of the Illinois Hospital Association, advocated separation of actual hospital expenses
from medical education, saying that he thought this might
cut as much as fifteen percent from the patient's bill.
Medical education was not properly a "hospital" cost at
all and should be borne by the American educational system in one way or another, Danielson said.

Excellent as the idea might be, on the record of a decade
even so vital a change as this would only mean holding
the line on costs for one or perhaps two years, and would
require an outright reorganization of the hospital system,
at no one knew what cost. And then what? Hospital costs
would continue to rise, as they had risen from $15 a day on
the average in 1950 to $45 a day on the average in 1965.
At this rate of increase, costs could not but rise beyond the reach of the average American family, let alone
of the poor. For a time the lag might be made up by deficit
operations, increase in charity work, or some kind of partial subsidy on a local, state, or even national level. Medicare was just such a measure, offering to a part of the population—the elders—an improved health program. But
how much of an answer was that for the nation as a whole?
And would such a program, for the aged alone, bring
America into the forefront of those nations which had
shown earlier concern and greater progress in health care?
As the United States talked about Medicare for the aged,
Canada was moving toward Medicare for all its citizens—
a government-backed national health-insurance program
which would provide hospitalization for citizens of every
age.

There were other hospital problems. Doctors and hospital men began to speak out in 1965 about thousands of unnecessary operations and other forms of malpractice in the United States. Malpractice was becoming a serious health problem. During the five years before 1965 more than a thousand disciplinary actions were reported against physicians and surgeons by state boards of medical examiners, and most of the complaints were based on instances of incompetence.[7] The public began to learn of carelessness and ignorance in hundreds of America's 7,000 hospitals; the number of malpractice suits rose year after year until 10,000 suits were filed in 1965. Only two-thirds of America's hospitals could meet the standards established by the Joint Commission on Accreditation, the organization founded by physicians, surgeons, and hospital administrators to police American hospitals.[8]

What had happened to American hospitals to create so many problems?

Actually, the hospitals seemed more victims than villains, victims of sociological change that has moved more rapidly than the health leaders of America appreciated, or were willing to accept. Only in 1965, with the passage of the Medicare bill, did the American Medical Association, for example, accept the demand for change in the health system as the wish of the American public.

Quietly, but surely, by the middle of the twentieth century the role of the American hospital had changed drastically. Quite in reverse of the past, hospitals devoted 70 percent of their time and effort to the cure of disease, and only 30 percent to "hotel" facilities. The hospital of the 1960's was on the way to becoming the health center of the community.

All this meant that the hospital was constantly adding —adding personnel, equipment, departments, and ser-

vices. It meant that the hospital was assuming new responsibilities while trying to cope with all the old problems
and old responsibilities, and in many cases while hampered
by an organizational or management system that was a
hangover from the old days of hotel-hospitals.

The hospital was also facing a new awareness, by public
and government, of the responsibilities of hospitals. Too
often this awareness arose in confusion and was surrounded by confusion, as it was in a quarrel that arose in
late 1965 between United States Senator Robert Kennedy
of New York and Governor Nelson Rockefeller of the same
state, over the problem of New York's hospitalization of
mental defectives. Perhaps unknowingly, when he visited a
number of his state's mental hospitals and criticized unfavorably the conditions he found in them, Senator Kennedy
put his finger on a most serious national problem: the
problem of mental illness. In the United States, 41 percent
of the nation's hospital beds were devoted to mental illness, or mental defection. On average, less than one new
patient is admitted per bed in mental hospitals each year,
while about 30 patients use each bed in the general hospitals.[9] Yet one in ten Americans were said, in 1965, to be
suffering from some variety of mental illness. Obviously
the hospital treatment of mental illness in America was
lagging; and yet New York, with all its deficiencies, had
the most advanced system in the United States when Senator Kennedy criticized it. The problem of mental institutions in New York, as elsewhere, was to determine who
was responsible for this aspect of hospital care. In New
York the state had assumed this responsibility for a hundred years, although private, city, and county institutions
existed in 1965 for mental treatment. One aspect of the
quarrel between Senator Kennedy and Governor Rocke-

feller was the governor's insistence that mental illness was
a state problem, and the Senator's insistence that a general
conference be called to see how private, city, county, and
state health units could take advantage of a multiplicity of
federal programs for mental-health care.

Here lay a simple example of the complexity of all hospitalization. What could be said of mental-health care, including its grave inadequacies, could be said of all hospital
care. America, in 1966, had many different hospital programs; many different areas of jurisdiction, established
by law and by custom; many different points of view about
hospitals and health care; and so many different kinds of
hospitals that they must be examined historically and by
groups before the hospital problem begins to make any
sense at all.

The hospital has a long history as an institution of mercy
and charity. Following the collapse of the Roman Empire,
the care of the sick and wounded became a responsibility
of the Christian church in Europe, and the American hospital is descended from this tradition. In the sixth century
of the Christian era, as the Roman Empire dissolved,
students of medicine fled to the monasteries for protection.
One of the first great repositories of medical information
and practice was the Benedictine monastery at Monte
Cassino in Italy. Other Benedictines took medical knowledge to Oxford, Cambridge, and Winchester in England,
to Tours in France, to Fulda in Germany, and to St. Gall
in what is now Switzerland. Soon hospitals were built in
these places as parts of the monasteries.

At St. Gall, for example, the monks planted herbs to
start their pharmacy. At first they provided arrangements
for the housing of six ill persons and a special room for the
physician to use for examination and treatment.

Control of these early hospitals rested in the hands of the church. One of the most important hospitals of the Dark Ages was located at Salerno, south of Naples, just above the top of the instep of the Italian boot. It was founded in the seventh century and a hundred years later was known through Europe for its charitable works and for the quality of its treatment. A medical school was established in connection with the hospital, and this might be called the first Western teaching hospital.[10]

The burden of hospitalization became too much for the church to bear alone as early as the year 1000, and thereafter a succession of popes and church councils began to restrict the medical activity of monks and priests until it was forbidden altogether, except in the most exceptional of circumstances; the running of hospitals and medical treatment were taking too much time from religious duties.

At about this time, during the Crusades, special orders of monks were created to undertake the operation of hospitals and the care of the sick. These were the Knights Hospitalers, formed to answer a need that arose during the eleventh century, when many crusaders and pilgrims to the Holy Land fell ill. Originally these knights (all must be of noble birth) were organized as the Knights of the Hospital of St. John of Jerusalem. Later their order was transferred to Cyprus, then to Rhodes, and finally to Malta, where its hospital work ceased.

With the eleventh century and the Knights Hospitalers, the word *Hospital* came into general use in Europe, derived through Old French from the Latin *hospitalis*, or place of rest. The first nursing order, that of the Augustine nuns, was organized around 1150; the need was imperative because only the very lowest classes of society, outside the church, were willing to undertake the disagreeable tasks of nursing for the tiny bit of money that hospitals could afford to pay.

During the Renaissance, hospitals were frequented only by the poor and the dying who had no other place to go. Anyone who had a bed with a roof over it chose to suffer his illness at home, treated by his physician, bled by his surgeon-barber, and nursed by his servants or his family. The hospital was known as a pest-house, and often, in its dungeons, the insane were confined in chains.

St. Bartholomew's Hospital was founded in London in 1123, and for four centuries it existed as a religious institution, but in the sixteenth century Henry VIII endowed the hospital with funds of the crown, thus beginning the public support of hospitals rather than religious support.

Yet the religious hospitals continued to be preferred, for in them the sick were treated humanely. The public hospitals were nearly intolerable. The poor and diseased were abhorred by the well-to-do, and work in hospitals acquired a stigma that it was to lose only by degrees. Until the middle of the twentieth century the attendants, scrubwomen, and other service personnel in hospitals were drawn from the lowest groups of society and were paid accordingly.

The most common architectural form of the hospital developed during the Renaissance, and was to be used into the twentieth century. This was the building that rose high into the air, constructed around an inner court, giving little light and ventilation. There was another method of building hospitals, but it did not appeal to city dwellers. This was the pavilion plan, developed in France. It called for wards housed in wings, not more than three stories in height, exposed to light and air on three sides, radiating out from a central structure which housed the administration and service facilities.

The hospital came to North America in the sixteenth century; the first hospital there was that of Jesus of Nazareth, founded in Mexico in 1524. The Hotel-Dieu in Quebec was founded in 1639, and the Hotel-Dieu in Montreal, in 1644, by missionaries who had been given funds by several important noble families of France.

The first attempt in the thirteen colonies to care for the sick on a regular public basis was the Philadelphia Almshouse, founded by the Society of Friends in 1713, which became an insane asylum.[11] The first hospital built to care for the sick and injured in what was to be the United States was Pennsylvania Hospital in Philadelphia, established in 1751.

Thereafter during the eighteenth century, hospitals were organized as charitable institutions for the treatment of the poor, supported by the wealthier citizens of the community. In many cases the professors of the medical schools were active in creating these hospitals, at least partly so they would have clinical facilities for instruction of their students.

Simultaneously, in New York, another pattern was developing. One might say that it began in 1734, when Mayor Robert Lurting asked the common council to establish a municipal workhouse. Northwest of Beekman swamp, east of what is now Cortlandt Street, and southwest of what is now Park Row but was then the muddy Boston Post Road, a two-story building was erected, 24 feet wide and 56 feet long. The cellar was provided with a whipping post for unruly slaves and an iron cage for the insane. The first floor held a dining room, the apartment

of the warden, and housing for inmates; on the second
floor, in the room at the west end, was an infirmary. This
was the beginning of Bellevue Hospital, in 1965 New
York's 2,600-bed city-owned hospital. Bellevue was to lead
the way in the development of another hospital philosophy
in America: that of civic responsibility for public health.

This social advance came to New York for a very good
reason: the city was often visited during the eighteenth
century by plague, yellow fever, and typhus. During the
great epidemic of 1798 more than 2,000 of New York's
36,000 people perished from yellow fever. In 1819 a
French ship from Martinique brought the fever again. In
conformity with the practice of the time, the vessel was
quarantined, and when several crew members were found
to be sick it was kept anchored off Governor's Island for
24 days. Then the quarantine officer went aboard, inspected the ship, and found the captain dead of yellow
jack. A few days later the quarantine officer fell ill with
the fever, as did five members of his staff, and soon they
were all dead.

The fever spread to the city and settled in the slum
area on the west side of the Old Slip, at the tip of Manhattan near South Street. The deaths began. A few weeks
later another disease struck the city—typhus—and another 1,850 New Yorkers came down with that affliction.
The slum areas were evacuated, the growing Bellevue
Hospital was filled, and still there were not enough doctors or enough hospital accommodations. For a time,
everyone agreed that public health was a city responsibility.

But they soon forgot the plague and the city hospital
became a repository for the insane. The political chieftains
of New York refused the doctors the funds they wanted.

Dr. Benjamin Ogden, head of the hospital, was ignored
when he pleaded for help. In disgust he quit, but was
persuaded to return in 1837. He struggled on against public and official indifference, amid the suffering poor who
lay in filthy blankets, without sheets or pillow cases. The
patients were given no clothing, and some of them had
nothing at all to wear. There were shortages of medicines
and not even rags for bandages.

This situation continued until 1847, when another catas-
trophe came to New York. Again it was a typhus epidemic,
beginning in June and lasting all summer.

Finally, in this atmosphere of death, came a major
change which was to affect hospital conditions in every
part of America. The aldermen of New York were pushed
into naming a board of nine physicians and surgeons to
take charge of Bellevue. This new administration soon
reduced the death rate in the hospital from 30 percent to
nine percent. They began the teaching tradition there in
1849. Dr. James Wood, the guiding force behind this
change, soon established a board of governors, which included some of the most respected businessmen of the
city, and they undertook a program of study of hospital
management elsewhere. In 1869, Bellevue hospital inaugurated the first ambulance service in the world, with
two horse-drawn vehicles.[12]

At about the same time, a Metropolitan Board of Health
was formed, to oversee the operation of the city hospital
and public health. In 1872, social service in hospitals was
begun by the Ladies Visiting Committee, a group of prominent New York women led by Miss Louisa Schuyler,[13]
who persuaded the city health commissioner to go to
London to visit Florence Nightingale's school of nursing
at St. Thomas's Hospital, although there was not then a

single trained nurse or a nursing school in America. As a result, America's first nursing school was founded at Bellevue Hospital, on May 1, 1873.

Haltingly, Bellevue progressed, and with it New York City's health services, until in 1913 those services led the nation. New York State, however, was far behind until that year, when Governor William Sulzer ordered the reorganization of the state health department.

The nineteenth century had been marked by several developments in hospitalization in America. One was the growing acceptance by various states of their responsibility to treat and care for the mentally ill. Campaigns such as those of Dorothea Dix brought about the creation of mental hospitals in most states. Local governments began to take responsibility for the treatment of the old, the chronically ill, the poor, and the victims of accidents and contagious diseases. Church and other charity hospitals became havens for the poor, although the wealthy or well-to-do continued to be treated in private hospitals or at home.[14]

The first quarter of the twentieth century was the period of most rapid growth in the development of American hospitals. The ratio of available hospital beds to patients rose in 1928 to 7.4 per thousand, putting the United States in this respect very close to the leaders in hospital practices, but this growth was halted by the great American depression. After the depression a new pattern began to emerge. The government took responsibility for chronic and difficult cases which involved long-term hospitalization.[15] Government hospitals, by 1948, comprised 30 percent of the total hospitals and 70 percent of the beds, but only 26 percent of admissions to hospitals.

The non-government hospitals, with only about 30 percent of the beds, handled 70 percent of the patients. Those comparative statistics changed very little in the next eighteen years, for the number of hospitals and number of beds changed relatively little.

Government hospitals were responsible, from the beginning, to the agency of government to which they belonged. Thus the military services operated their own hospitals, the U.S. Public Health Service operated its own hospitals, the Veterans Administration and other agencies were in charge of their own programs. Hospitals of state and local governments traditionally were also responsible to the government agencies they served, but very early it became apparent that standardization of health services within a state could be enforced only through the state public health department, and so in all states the hospitals of a state were licensed by such departments and were inspected and forced to meet certain minimum standards established by the states.

After the American Hospital Association was formed in 1899 it soon became apparent that state regulation was spotty and sometimes unsound. Gradually there arose a demand for standardization of medical and hospital standards. In 1904 the American Medical Association created its committee on medical education and hospitals. Out of this came the famous Flexner report of 1910, which directly revolutionized medical education, and less directly brought about radical changes in hospitalization. In 1913 the American College of Surgeons was established, partly to set standards for hospital construction, administration, and equipment, and it established minimum standards for hospitals. Two years later the American College of Physicians was established, to promote high standards in the practice of internal medicine.

These organizations together established the Joint Commission on Accreditation of Hospitals in 1953 and began to work to standardize certain practices and administration of *all* kinds of hospitals in the United States. Until the Eisenhower administration laid the ground for federal standardization of health practices with the establishment of the Department of Health, Education and Welfare, the Joint Commission enforced the *only* national standards for hospitals in the United States.

In 1965 only about 60 percent of American hospitals were accredited by this Joint Commission.[16] It was not necessarily true that a hospital was inferior because it was not accredited; it might be too new to be accredited, and in fact be better than accredited hospitals; or it might have been refused accreditation and have corrected the difficulty in the meantime. The Joint Commission's standards in 1965 were not so demanding that a fairly good hospital could not meet them. In the survey made for the Teamster's Union by the Columbia University School of Public Health and Administrative Medicine, university surveyors commented adversely on the minimal standards accepted by the Joint Commission, calling this a "problem still of public concern." [17]

Many hospitals in America have had accreditation trouble in recent years, hospitals both large and small. Cook County Hospital in Chicago, the second largest in the country, is one of these. In 1962 the Joint Commission placed Cook County Hospital on probation for the second time in a decade, listing some 20 violations of the hospital commission's code. These pertained to shortage of nurses, overcrowding, obsolescence of the X-ray department, and improper handling of the obstetrical section.

Had Cook County Hospital lost its accreditation, more

than 100,000 people would have been forced to look for new hospital facilities. That many people were admitted there in 1963, and another quarter of a million were treated as outpatients. After a six-man team inspected the hospital for two days in the summer of 1964, enough improvement was found so that the hospital was given a three-year accreditation by the Commission; however this was accompanied by a warning that more improvement was needed.

That three-year approval was a sign that real improvement had been made at Cook County Hospital. The Joint Commission might have given one-year approval, as it did to about twenty percent of the hospitals it examined. In 1963 the Joint Commission examined 1,743 hospitals, approved 1,307 of them for three years, approved 342 of them for one year, and refused accreditation to 94. The most common deficiency found was a failure to keep adequate medical records. Medical records should show the course of treatment of patients. From the point of view of public health, such complete clinical records are essential to the community, since through such records medical scientists can learn more about disease.

From the point of view of the patient, medical records might save his life. In a second hospitalization, for example, a consultation of the records might reveal some abnormality or trend in his first hospitalization which bears upon apparently new symptoms.

Another common default of hospitals was failure to enforce the rule that doctors must hold clinical reviews of all cases and findings, as a safeguard for the patients against misdiagnosis by their family physician or any other doctor who treated them.

Doctors assume serious responsibilities of medical management in hospitals, and the Joint Commission examined the manner in which they carried these out. Some hospitals were refused accreditation because they did not establish adequate qualifications for staff doctors. In New York City it was discovered that operations were being performed in a non-accredited hospital by doctors *whose names did not appear on any known medical list.*

Every accredited hospital must take extreme caution in medical and surgical care. The Joint Commission regulated this care through two local committees: a tissue committee, which examined surgical procedures and made certain that doctors were not performing unnecessary operations; and a medical procedures committee, which analyzed the care given by doctors in the hospital. A large number of hospitals were refused accreditation because their tissue committees failed to function properly. This failure might have resulted from carelessness, yet the presumption was that the doctors did not want to investigate the operating practices of their peers on the staff. The first safeguard here was the examination of excised tissues by a pathologist, and in 1963, 50 hospitals were refused accreditation because they did not employ the services of a pathologist, even on a visiting basis.

The Joint Commission also demanded that hospitals maintain an autopsy rate of 20 percent, to check on the procedures of the hospital and its staff. Some hospitals found autopsies a great waste of time. In one Illinois hospital, after a man had died of mysterious causes his family wanted an autopsy, not because they suspected the hospital or doctors, for the patient had been ill for a long time, but because they believed that determining the actual cause of death would help medical science. The hospital refused to do an autopsy unless the family paid $50, and the family indigantly refused.

The Joint Commission's questions were sharp and pointed, and all of them were germane to the safety of patient and community. One requirement called for the hospital to carry out regular drills for a mass casualty plan —the best protection the community could have in case of sudden disaster such as a tornado, earthquake, or explosion. Another simple requirement was for regular fire drills, such as those held by schools and other public institutions. Simple, yet 53 hospitals were denied accreditation for ignoring this safety precaution. Hospitals were also rejected by the Joint Commission because they did not maintain the required consultants in various specialties, they were careless in maintenance of the nursery for the newborn, they permitted fire hazards, they were careless or incompetent in keeping up dietary standards, and they did not carry out adequate procedures in safeguarding surgical patients.

In 1965 the Joint Commission's standards were under examination by some medical leaders, such as teachers at the Columbia University School of Public Health, yet even if the standards were as high as might be expected, more than four million Americans that year went into hospitals unprotected by those standards. Some of those four million, in states where health department inspection was particularly lax, were protected by nothing at all.

Chapter Two

THE VOLUNTARY HOSPITAL

Hospitals can be divided into three general classes, based on method of finance and operation: the voluntary hospital, the government hospital, and the proprietary or profit-making hospital.

The most common hospital in all the American experience is the voluntary, non-profit, community hospital. It had been formed to meet the basic needs of the community, as a place for the sick to be housed. By far the largest number of American hospitals were voluntary non-profit hospitals, organized by people in the communities for the benefit of all. There were 3,400 of these in 1964. (State and local government hospitals totaled 1,400, and proprietary hospitals, just under 900.) One of the largest, most complex and most successful voluntary hospitals is New York Hospital in the nation's largest city. It is also one of the oldest, having been chartered by King George III in 1771.

The purpose of New York Hospital was stated in a petition to the King that year, "purpose being to establish a public hospital." The form was created: New York Hospital is operated by The Society of the New York Hospital. Its Board of Governors consists of 27 of the most wealthy and influential citizens of New York City. Among the names listed on the board are Burden, Loeb, Bliss, Osborne, Whitney, and Rockefeller—all names well known in the history of New York and sometimes in American finance and statesmanship.

In 1965 the hospital occupied a large complex of buildings on 68th Street in Manhattan, near the East River. Including a special mental-illness department located in Westchester county, the hospital had 1,578 beds for patients. A third of these were in wards, which the hospital prefers to call pavilions, and about a quarter were in semi-private rooms, which meant two beds to a room. There were 162 private rooms in the hospital, plus 109 beds in the Payne Whitney Psychiatric Clinic, and 350 beds in the Westchester division.

This hospital treated 35,000 bed patients in 1964, nearly half of them in the wards, or charitable department, but that is only a part of the story. It also treated nearly 31,500 patients at the emergency pavilion, and 45,000 patients in the out-patient and clinic departments. It maintained clinics to treat every kind of illness, from speech and hearing difficulties to varicose veins.

New York Hospital was the most complicated type of American hospital for another reason: it was a teaching and research institution as well as a general hospital. Its three city blocks also contained the Cornell University Medical College, and a school of nursing. As a teaching hospital and a treatment center, the hospital offered its patients the newest and best in American medical care.

More than two thousand doctors were on the staff. It kept special departments for study as well as practice of anesthesiology, neurology, obstetrics and gynecology, pathology, pediatrics, psychiatry, radiology, and surgery.

Anyone could come to New York Hospital for treatment. Getting into the hospital as a patient was not nearly so much a question of money as was generally believed. Although private, paying patients were asked to be sure that they could pay the bill before they were admitted, unless they had hospital insurance, the wards operated in 1964 at only 75 percent of capacity, which meant that overall there was room for more free treatment, or charity treatment. (The highest occupation rate in the wards was in surgery, which ran at 92 percent of capacity—very high; the lowest in obstetrics and gynecology, which ran at 58 percent of capacity—very low.[1]) Getting into New York Hospital was a question of applying at one of the clinics, or of coming in at the arrangement of one of the physicians on the staff.

Once in, the patient could not ask for better care or treatment than he would receive at New York Hospital. It was operated, like most teaching hospitals, in the highest traditions of American public service.

"Teaching hospital" is a term that goes back to the early days of Bellevue. Hospitals were—and are—used for medical education, and some of them are connected with medical colleges in one way or another.

As a private institution undertaking a basic task of public service, New York Hospital lost money in 1965. Its assets amounted to $81 million, including nearly $40 million of investments. These investments had been made over the years from moneys given to the hospital by donors and in bequests. (Some six hundred or so donors gave

$10,000 or more each to the hospital in a century, and many legacies, large and small, were left to the hospital. Some donors endowed beds, at a cost of $10,000 each.)

The hospital expected to lose money in its treatment of patients, but neither this hospital nor any other voluntary hospital could lose too much money in the 1960's and survive. The losses had to be made up in some way—the bills had to be paid, and this was done in various manners described elsewhere. The point was that the voluntary community hospital, of which New York Hospital was a prime example, operated only in the public interest. Its charges represented the allocation of cost to beds and for other services. In 1964 New York Hospital lost $3.63 for every day a bed patient spent in the hospital, and $7.00 for every patient visit to the out-patient department.[2] Whether or not one might quarrel with the hospital's manner of allocating expenses (who is to pay for medical education—the patients?) the fact was that New York Hospital represented the ancient concept of hospital charity: open the doors to the people, let the well-to-do pay their own way and assume part of the cost of the poor, let the rich support the hospital as a charity, and let the poor come without exception, paying what they could, or paying nothing. That was the voluntary hospital system in its essence.

Another typical voluntary hospital, much smaller than New York Hospital, was Sharon Hospital, in Sharon, Connecticut. This hospital had approximately 100 beds. It served a large area in three states; it was located near the point where Connecticut, Massachusetts, and New York meet. It was a community hospital providing a wide range of services to rich and poor without distinction—or nearly without distinction. The rich were likely to go into a private room, and the poor into a ward, but this was to be expected in the pattern of American hospitalization. Sharon Hospital had no financial requirement for entrance; no guarantee of any amount was needed, no matter where the patient had come from.

Some voluntary hospitals were operated by religious organizations. One such was the Mother Cabrini Memorial Hospital, in New York's Washington Heights district at Edgecomb Avenue near 163rd Street, run by the Missionary Sisters of the Sacred Heart, once a part of the health and hospitals section of the New York Diocese's organized Catholic charities. However, Mother Cabrini Hospital became a victim of changing times and the changing social mores of New York City.

The hospital was opened in 1936. Its last building was dedicated in 1939. So, it was a quarter of a century old (in the hospital development of the previous decade this made it very old indeed). That was not the major problem. Obsolescence of equipment, and even of the interior arrangement of the hospital, might have been cured by extensive alterations. No one could alter the changing face of New York, however, and that *was* the problem.

In the years just before World War II this area was a busy Italian section of the city. At the end of the war the Italian population began to move out and Puerto Ricans and Negroes began to move in. The difference was noticeable immediately in the operations of the hospital; not because the Sisters behaved any differently to the new population, but because far more of the people in the area were poor people who sought treatment at free clinics and city hospitals. The beds of the hospital were often empty, many bills were unpaid, and the medical staff of the hospital—private physicians—discovered that their incomes were dropping although their costs and the time they gave

to charity were increasing. Slowly, the staff physicians began to leave the area.

By 1964 it had become painfully apparent that the hospital had outlived its usefulness, and it was closed, to
reopen later as a center for chronic illness.

Mother Cabrini Hospital was a Roman Catholic hospital. That did not mean, however, that only Roman Catholics became patients there. Although it was once true that
special sects maintained their own hospitals, there was
relatively little religious discrimination or religious difference among hospitals in the 1960's. There could not be
discrimination, at least not visible discrimination, because
federal policies of the 1960's forbade it. No hospital could
receive federal funds, Medicare or other, if it discrimi-
nated against anyone for reasons of race, creed, color, or
national origin. Few "discriminating" hospitals would be
able to survive after 1965 in the face of federal disapproval of fund and payment requests.

Earlier voluntary hospitals had been founded by religious groups, as noted. The Roman Catholics led all others, perhaps, because the Catholic tradition of hospital
charity came to America from older and more experienced
Europe. In 1839 a Colored Home and Hospital was established in New York, to serve the Negroes who came to
that city. In 1849 came St. Vincent's Hospital, built by the
Catholic Sisters of Charity. In 1852 Mt. Sinai was founded,
called then the Jews' Hospital in New York. Why was a
Jewish hospital needed? Because there *was* discrimination
then, and at that time, with a half million people crowd-
ing Manhattan Island, there were 10,000 Jews among
them, quite enough to support and find the need for a
hospital of their own. When the Jews' Hospital opened its
doors, its board of trustees voted that it should not accept

any patients other than Jews, except in cases of accident. But the Civil War put an end to hospital sectarianism by the New York Jews; they opened the wards of the Jews' Hospital in 1861 to all wounded soldiers who were brought there, and by 1865 discrimination had ended. It took some time for the general public to accept this change; really the change was not accepted in New York until the state legislature in 1866 made the name of the hospital Mt. Sinai Hospital. Then the hospital began to be known as nonsectarian.

In the 1960's racial discrimination still existed in hospitals, but hardly of the variety of a century earlier, when discrimination was known by the more genteel euphemism of sectarianism.

Within the general classification of voluntary hospitals there were many special hospitals. New York City supported nearly 100 non-profit hospitals of various kinds, ranging from those operated by Catholic and other religious organizations to specialty hospitals, such as the Manhattan Eye, Ear and Throat Hospital, the Hospital for Joint Diseases, the Hospital for Special Surgery, several special women's hospitals, and the Memorial Sloan-Kettering Cancer Center, a complex group of hospitals and research facilities dedicated to the destruction of cancer.

Many of these large hospitals had clinics of their own. In dealing with cancer, the Memorial Sloan-Kettering group maintained a regular checkup service, trying to follow its patients for the remainder of their lives in the interest of research.

What would happen if a man were suddenly stricken with a heart attack on the sidewalk on East 68th Street in New York City, just outside the block-long buildings of the Sloan-Kettering Institute, Memorial Hospital, and James Ewing Hospital? The patient would probably be rushed to New York Hospital's emergency pavilion, two blocks away, and would not be brought into Memorial's complex at all. The reason: Memorial Hospital was in 1965 a specialty hospital, and it was not equipped, nor were its personnel's duties scheduled to give the best in emergency treatment. Every hospital professional should be able and willing to give emergency assistance. Memorial Hospital doctors have gone out into the street with their little black bags to treat the injured; but the hospital is not that kind of a hospital, and it would be a disservice to its own special patients for the professional staff to try to carry such an additional load.

This misunderstanding sometimes turns visitors and casual observers against these hospitals.

New York Hospital's financial condition in the 1960's was typical of the large community hospitals. In New York City, the patients who could not pay cost the city's voluntary hospitals $33 million a year, those who *would* not pay cost $20 million, and the training of medical personnel cost $20 million. What did this mean? A hospital like New York Hospital must live on its fat, if it had any. New York Hospital in 1964 spent $30 million, and received only $26 million from patient care, in one way or another. The difference was made up by several different methods. First came the moneys taken out of the Fund for Medical Progress, a joint fund-raising program conducted by the hospital and Cornell University Medical School. This came to $600,000. Then came funds designated for special purposes, money from the Greater New York Fund (the local community chest), and income from trusts and investments. Still, the public relations department of the hospital, which handled its private fund-raising, had to find nearly a million dollars, and the deficit for the year was still nearly $200,000.

Obviously New York Hospital was taxing every resource in 1965 to continue its high standards of care and education. Something had to give—particularly when rooms in that hospital might cost $100 a day within ten years. Who could afford such costs? Millionaires, certainly, but not only millionaires need the quiet that private rooms can bring. Other hospitals, undertaking building programs, had come to the conclusion that small units, sometimes private, sometimes semi-private, were scarcely harder to construct or more expensive to maintain than larger units. It was not the bed space that cost so much money in the 1960's. Nursing alone cost $10.6 million in New York Hospital in 1964, almost thirty percent of the total cost of running the hospital. Obviously, from the standpoint of a cost accountant, the community hospital was a nightmare.

This would be less true when Medicare began to make its presence felt in the hospital picture, for the federal government would reimburse hospitals for actual costs, rather than paying a per diem or a fixed rate that did not meet the overall costs. In time this might make itself felt in all hospital bills.

Forgetting the cost of patient care for a moment, let us examine the financial and administrative plight of hospitals in the 1960's. For a quarter of a century they had been living with the Hill-Burton act, which gave matching federal funds to hospitals for new construction. Yet, while billions were spent on new construction, in 1965 the American Hospital Association had to ask Congress for a half billion dollars just to keep hospitals at their *current* level.

The basic advances in hospitals and medical education

in America can be traced back to 1910 and Dr. Abraham
Flexner's report which revolutionized American medical
education. Until that time American medical education
and hospitalization were both far behind the systems of
Europe and threatened to fall further behind. The title
of doctor did not mean much. Medically knowledgeable
people found it useful to ask what kind of doctor, and
what kind of school the doctor had attended, for a doctor's degree was easily obtainable at homeopathic schools
and others. Few medical schools devoted time to clinical
training.

The Flexner study brought about the establishment of
new standards for medical schools. The schools became
affiliated with hospitals, and they were classified by the
American Medical Association as A, B, or C schools, depending on their ability to meet the standards established
for medical education. Soon the B and C schools began
affiliating with hospitals and upgrading their teaching—
or they closed their doors. By 1960 all American medical
schools were A schools.

For hospitals, the direct result of the Flexner report and
of the new attention given to health problems was a building boom. In the second decade of the twentieth century
more hospitals were built than in any previous ten-year
period of American history. Most of these were voluntary
hospitals.

Most hospitals managed to weather the depression of
the 1930's, but in the 1940's their troubles suddenly inten-
sified. Advances in medical knowledge brought pressures
for new techniques and new expenses. Inflation brought a
spiral of expense. Increased social consciousness brought
higher wages and higher hospital costs. Obsolescence
brought the headaches of rebuilding. The shifting of the

American population brought still another problem. The
shift was almost entirely to the west. California's population numbered 7,000,000 in 1940; 10,500,000 in 1950; and
15,700,000 in 1960. But the number of hospital beds did
not increase in such a ratio; society could not move so fast.
California, with perhaps a million fewer people than New
York, had just slightly more than half as many hospital
beds as New York in 1964.[3]

The voluntary hospitals were hit hardest by these
changes. Unlike the government hospitals, they could not
depend upon taxes. Unlike the hospitals run privately for
profit (called "proprietary hospitals"), they could not refuse to give services for which they were not paid.

In the 1940's, government began to come to the assistance of America's hospitals, saving hundreds of voluntary
hospitals from hopeless obsolescence or even abandon-
ment. The first major government assistance was the Hill-
Burton law, which gave matching funds for the construction of hospitals. This brought about a rapid increase in
the growth of voluntary hospitals. By 1964 the federal
government had spent $3.8 billion under this program to
add nearly 300,000 beds to American hospitals.

Still, the voluntary hospitals were in trouble. This was
before the passage of the Medicare bill, which even the
most conservative estimated would increase the need for
hospital beds by about ten percent. As of 1964 and 1965,
according to the chairman of the American Medical Association Council on Medical Service, hospital beds were becoming obsolete at the same rate that new hospital beds
were being made available.

Even in hospital construction the patient could not get
away from paying a share of cost. Hospitals often had to
borrow money in order to build additions and to modern-

ize. They paid as high as 6.5% in interest and carrying charges, and this had to be passed along to patients and members of health-insurance plans.

The cost of hospital construction in the 1960's was very high, higher in a way than construction of ordinary buildings, because hospitals in cities must be relatively noiseless places, and heavy, soundproof construction was generally out of style in America. In 1964 New York Hospital proposed to build a new medical research building, and this would cost $9,000,000. It wanted to expand the Woman's Clinic, and this would mean spending $1,000,000 to complete and equip a new surgical floor and $2,000,000 to reorganize the elevator system, and at the end, with all its modern equipment, this part of the hospital would still be very much like the rest of the hospital, old in style.

The hospitals faced serious problems in a time of inflation because their endowment funds were decreasing, both in fact and in value; in fact because taxes caused fewer people to leave large sums to hospitals, and from time to time the hospitals were forced to dip into capital to meet operating deficit; in value because the dollar of endowment left in 1925 was worth perhaps 40 cents in purchasing power in 1965.

In 1963, in Massachusetts, hospitals looked around anxiously for ways to solve their problems. (They envied one hospital in Rhode Island that operated a factory and made profits from it, but there were not very many situations like that in America.) The Boston hospitals, in particular, found themselves facing intolerable deficits, year after year. Massachusetts General Hospital, a non-profit institution, was hurt very badly. In one year it had to take $1,500,000 from its endowment to meet running expenses, because neither Blue Cross nor state welfare agencies paid enough to take care of the costs. Even after "robbing" endowment funds, as Dr. John H. Knowles, director of the hospital called it, and overcharging private patients, those with private insurance, and those with Blue Cross full contracts, the deficit was hardly met.

Massachusetts General became pugnacious and went to court to solve its problems. The state legistlature sent in an investigating commission to examine the subject. After months of examination nothing much came forth, except two reports which were almost opposite in their approaches to the problem, and neither of which solved it. The day of federal control of hospitals moved a little closer.

The cost of equipment in the voluntary hospitals was a great expense. This cost was the cost of keeping current, adding new machinery and devices and avoiding obsolescence. Much of what used to be called special equipment was no longer special in 1966. Many hospitals had cobalt therapy units for the treatment of cancer, which might cost $150,000; pace-maker defibrillator equipment to start and control hearts that stopped on the operating table, at about $5,000 per unit; expensive electroencephalograph equipment to measure the action of the brain; heart-lung machines to oxygenate blood and make heart surgery possible; artificial kidneys that keep people with kidney disease alive where once they died.

Such equipment had gone far beyond the big teaching hospitals. A hospital in Anchorage, of about 100 beds, had invested $50,000 in equipment in two years; a larger hospital in Reno had secured $500,000 in gifts to purchase new equipment. A Houston hospital administrator said that some specialized equipment in the hospital's radiology department had been financed by raising the price of X-rays.

One administrator noted that hardly had a piece of equipment been purchased than another manufacturer came up with another device that provided some additional way of treating or preventing disease. "If one life is saved by a more advanced instrument than has been known before, it seems that its purchase is justified," he said. The most quickly discarded equipment, for reasons of obsolescence, came in the cardiovascular department, said another: "We find that equipment is often improved before we have received the value of the equipment that is being replaced."

Two common problems of obsolescence were found in the obstetrical and pediatrics wards. One hospital in Miami, only five years old, discovered in 1965 that its patient load in the obstetrical department fell fifty percent, which meant that its use of space was wasteful. At the same time, reflecting earlier days, the pediatrics department grew. Could the hospital afford to turn its obstetrics ward into something else?

The Miami hospital could and did, but a hospital in Ponca City, Oklahoma, found that while the obstetrics department was only half-occupied most of the time, there were a few periods during each year when it was filled to overflowing. What was the hospital to do? It must maintain the facilities the public needs, even if the need is sporadic.

New York's Sloan-Kettering Institute and Memorial Hospital proposed to build in 1966 or so, modernizing its facilities. Among other plans was one to place the patient's rooms around a central core, so that the furthest distance a nurse need travel from her nursing station to a patient was 80 feet—cutting fifty feet off the present distance.

Waterbury Hospital in Connecticut announced in the

spring of 1965 that it would spend $365,000 to improve patient and treatment facilities.

On what? Here are a few of the items: Two new elevators to the four floors, to allow the use of the single old north elevator as a service elevator. New quarters for the respiratory clinic, electroencephalograph laboratory, and electro-cardiology laboratory.

This represents a part of a 14-year hospital modernization program that began in 1951 with major additions: a new four-story wing, a new lobby, offices, a chapel, an aid-society pantry, a gift shop, a laundry, and a new wing for the nursing school.

In those fourteen years much of the hospital was revamped, too. A special care unit was opened, to conform to the new hospitalization idea of progressive care, in which surgical and other seriously ill patients are taken from round-the-clock observation and care into a rest and recuperation program in the period before their discharge when they need only minimal attention.

Besides the things that show, the hospital had put in a new sprinkler system to conform to safety practices and fire laws, and had modernized its electrical system, at a cost of about $70,000.

All this, then, gives us some idea of the cost of maintaining voluntary hospitals as modern centers for the care of America's people.

Chapter Three

GOVERNMENT
HOSPITALS

Only thirty percent of the hospitals of the United States are government hospitals, operated either by federal, state, county, city, or city-county agencies, or by hospital districts.[1] Yet these hospitals are far more important than their number would suggest. Government hospitals exist to handle special classes of people, such as members of the armed forces and veterans, or special health problems, such as mental illness or tuberculosis, or to serve the various government units in managing the health problems of a government area. Government hospitals are very much in the minority, yet they contain more hospital beds than any other kind of hospital, because federal, state, county and other governments have assumed the major responsibility for the care of the mentally ill and the retarded, tuberculars, and patients with other long-term illnesses.[2] Mental illness, for one, tends to be prolonged and expensive. Many of those confined to mental hospitals measure their stays in years. Few families can afford to pay the expenses of prolonged mental illness, or for the private care of a retarded child or mental defective.

The tendency in the two decades since the end of World War II was for a marked increase in the number of state and local government general hospitals. The number of these nearly doubled between 1946 and 1963, from 785 to 1,394, which meant huge increases in establishment and operating costs. Yet these general or short-term government hospitals had not increased nearly so markedly in the number of beds: from 133,000 to 168,000. What had happened to these hospitals was symbolic of what had happened to all hospitals. Their payroll costs had risen about seven hundred percent, from $140,000 in 1946 to $1,058,000,000 in 1963. The number of employees per 100 patients had risen from 129 in 1946 to 237 in 1963. Here was the explanation of the huge cost in a nutshell: the number of hospital workers per patient had nearly doubled in less than two decades, and the pay of these people had increased steadily. One can see why the increase in the number of hospitals did not necessarily mean a commensurate increase in the number of beds.

These figures are significant in studying the problems of all American hospitals. The fact that government and voluntary general hospitals have followed the same trends is an indication that the expenses of government hospitals represent generally good management, or as good as is available anywhere. One especially significant figure involves the length of stay of patients in government as compared with non-government hospitals. Patients who go to government hospitals tend to stay longer because the pressure of expense is not so heavy on them, if it exists at all. In 1963 patients in government hospitals remained on an average of eight and a half days for each admission. In

voluntary hospitals they remained only seven and a half
days.³ Again, historical comparison indicates a trend in
all hospitals: in 1946 patients in government hospitals
stayed 11.4 days, while those in voluntary hospitals remained on an average of 8.8 days. Part of this change is
due to advances in medicine which have enabled patients
to be made ambulatory earlier—but not all of it. Part of
it, too, is due to the extreme economic pressures brought
upon hospital and patient to get patients in and out of the
hospital quickly. It is significant that in the proprietary
hospitals there was much less change in length of stay in
those same years. In 1946 patients going into proprietary
hospitals stayed an average of about six and a half days,
and in 1963 a little longer than six days.

Government short-term hospitals come in every size
and variety. A comparison that brings home the vast range
of hospitals tagged "government institutions" is that between New York City's huge Bellevue general hospital
and the tiny county general hospital in Fairplay, Park
County, high in the Rocky Mountain region of Colorado.

Bellevue in 1963 maintained 2,646 beds. It admitted
45,000 patients. It employed nearly six thousand people,
and operated at a cost to the city of New York of $31,200,-
000. Bellevue was accredited by the Joint Commission on
Accreditation of Hospitals; it operated a cancer program
approved by the American College of Surgeons; it was
approved for residency and internship training by the
American Medical Association; it had medical school affiliation with several schools, including New York University and Cornell. It maintained hospital-controlled professional nursing schools for both men and women. It was
constantly building and rebuilding, adding units and special equipment, so as better to serve the people of New

York. It maintained service departments which brought the patient who had lost control of some faculty back as far toward normal as possible through physical therapy, and then it helped the patient find a job through its social service departments. It was a hospital for the acutely ill, the mentally ill, and those suffering from certain types of chronic illness. It could probably be said to be the most complete and most varied hospital in all America.

As noted in earlier chapters, Bellevue's "firsts" are many. For example, it was one of the earliest American hospitals to install radiocobalt therapy in the 1950's. It carried on medical research in scores of directions.

Bellevue was a public hospital, a government hospital. And so was the tiny county hospital in Fairplay, in Park County, Colorado. Bellevue had the advantages of medical school faculties, distinguished specialists, and the most modern equipment imaginable. In 1964 Fairplay hospital had hardly any advantages at all. Bellevue was an accredited hospital; Fairplay, in 1964, was about to lose the license it held from the Colorado State Board of Health. One of the few similarities between them was that they were both listed in the American Hospital Association's guide. Listing in the AHA guide, however, does not imply approval.

Fairplay hospital's story was not atypical of the problems of small government hospitals and small rural hospitals in America.

In the summer of 1964 Dr. Roy Cleere, Colorado's director of public health, announced that Fairplay Hospital's licence would be refused when it came up for renewal. Unless the county commissioners of Park County voted to replace the hospital with a new one the county would not have any approved facilities. This would mean considerable hardship, especially for the county's old and poor.

Fairplay Hospital was old and tired. It had begun life seventy-five years earlier as a private home, overlooking the old mining town of Fairplay. It had been a boarding house, and later the headquarters of the local Ku Klux Klan when that organization controlled Colorado politically in the 1920's. The building was converted to hospital use in 1929, but by hospital standards the conversion was never successful. Had not this sparsely populated county of the West needed a hospital of its own, the conversion would probably never have been countenanced. The operating room on the second floor of the hospital was reached by a winding staircase, and volunteer firemen were sometimes called to carry stretcher patients upstairs for surgery. The X-ray machine was closeted in a converted kitchen. Increasingly in recent years the Fairplay hospital failed to meet the state's health standards. Most serious were the complaints that the hospital had no fire detection system, no sprinkler system, no firedoors. It had open stairwells, inadequate fire exits, and not enough door and hall clearance. There was no safe storage place for oxygen cylinders, and there was direct contact between the operating room, sterilizing room, and delivery room. The kitchen had no sterilizing equipment at all.

As long as possible, various state inspectors overlooked these deficiencies, but in the last few years the state had grown reluctant to share the possible liability. How the hospital continued to be registered by the American Hospital Association might be puzzling, unless one knew that registration by that organization did *not* constitute approval of facilities.

Nevertheless, Fairplay Hospital was clean and neat, and the service it performed was useful to the area.

The State Health Department suggested that Fairplay Hospital be closed, patients be removed to the bigger cities, and an emergency clinic be built for Fairplay. In 1961 some taxpayers in Platte Canyon, between Fairplay and Denver, suggested the same. But by 1964 the increased use of the hospital facilities gave hope to those who wanted to keep their own hospital. Only 150 people had been admitted to the hospital that year, but 675 emergency cases had been treated, and 909 out-patients. Having no choice but to abandon the old building, the supporters of the hospital decided to try to raise the money for a small 20-bed hospital that would have eight beds for hospital patients and 12 beds for nursing-home or chronic patients, and would meet all the requirements of the Colorado state hospital licensing standards. The cost of construction would be about $300,000, roughly half of it obtainable from the federal government under the Hill-Burton act.

By the end of 1965 Fairplay had not solved its problem, but it was working on the problem, and its efforts were under the scrutiny of some fifteen other communities in Colorado which faced similar problems.

All persons concerned with American health recognize the obvious—that one cannot provide the same level of service for the 2,500 people of Park County, Colorado, that is provided for the 8,000,000 people of New York City. Just what are the minimal standards of hospitalization to which every American is entitled? That question will be answered only when one agency is given overall authority for the establishment of minimum health standards, whether this be a federal government agency or an agency combining government and the health professions.

As elsewhere, in Colorado the state's responsibility for hospital care—hospital care that is paid for from state funds—is usually limited to long-term or chronic illness, as distinct from short-term or acute illness and medical emergency. In an earlier era the pressing problem of all the states in this was tuberculosis, which was then difficult to treat. The picture has changed drastically in the twentieth century, in Colorado as everywhere else.

In 1963 Colorado maintained 92 hospitals of all kinds. Of these only two were tuberculosis hospitals—in the state that had been a center of tuberculosis treatment in the United States a half century before. The number of tuberculosis hospitals everywhere had been falling steadily, with medical science's advances in treatment and prevention of this debilitating and killing disease. In 1946 the country had 412 tuberculosis hospitals, housing 75,000 beds. In 1963 there were only 186 such hospitals, with 39,000 beds. In 1946, 85,000 people had been admitted to hospitals in America suffering from tuberculosis. In 1963, only 55,000 such patients were admitted.

But the comfort that might be obtained from these figures on tuberculosis would be shattered by examining the figures on mental illness. In 1946 the United States counted 476 non-federal psychiatric hospitals, with 568,-000 beds. In 1963 the number of hospitals had risen to only 499, and the number of beds to only 715,000, but admissions had *doubled* from 202,000 to 435,000, and the mental hospitals were occupied at the very high rate of 91 percent. Among the most serious hospital problems in America in 1966 were those of the mental hospitals, their low

level of financing, and the inadequacy of psychiatric treatment. One figure perhaps shows all this better than any
other: In 1963 the average expenditure per patient per day
in general hospitals was about $39, but the average expen-
diture in psychiatric hospitals, for all purposes, was only $6
per patient. Officials of the U.S. Public Health Service were
concerned because so little was being done to cure and discharge mental patients, and thus the mental hospitals were
overcrowded and would continue to be overcrowded until
the problem was solved, since federal health authorities
estimated that one in ten Americans was suffering from
some form of mental illness.

In a way, the existence of government mental and other
long-term hospitals tends to confuse the hospital picture,
for example in the number of hospital workers compared
with the number of patients. The mental hospitals and
long-term disease hospitals distort the general picture because in these there are only 40 hospital workers serving
each 100 patients, as compared to about 240 workers per
100 patients in all other hospitals, or six times as many.
On the average, then, there were about 130 hospital workers for every 100 patients in the 1960's, but that average
was most misleading, and in no way represented the serious problems faced by government hospitals, particularly
in long-range treatment.

The least prepossessing hospitals in America in the
1960's were the huge complexes used for the treatment of
mental illness and mental deficiency, and often simply as
dumps for humans who could not be integrated into American society. In every state of the union these hospitals
were harried by public disapproval, by obsolescence, and
by special personnel problems, many of these caused by

the undesirability of working in such drab and unpleasant surroundings.

Generally speaking, the states operate the mental hospitals. In New York, for example, more than 20 private institutions were licensed in 1965 by the New York State Department of Mental Hygiene to care for state mental patients, and twice that many private hospitals with psychiatric facilities were approved by the state, but by far the most cases of mental illness were served by the state's 29 institutions, including nineteen hospitals and nine schools for the mentally retarded. In 1965 the program, and some of these schools and institutions, were under critical investigation; still, the New York mental-hospital system was regarded as the most advanced in the nation. Its difficulties were those of any huge complex medical or hospital system: 84,000 patients were treated in those hospitals that year, and 21,000 others were receiving out-patient care. One hospital alone, at King's Park, Long Island, cared for 13,000 patients. Many abuses could be traced directly to the problem of size. As a remedy, in 1965, New York shifted from the building of large institutions to the building of hospitals of no more than 1,000 beds each.

How are such state hospital plans supported? In some states they draw their money from the state's general fund. In New York they are also supported by fees from patients, by Blue Cross fees, by Social Security, and by contributions from the families of patients. If a patient cannot pay, the services are free. They are also free at local clinics for out-patient care, and when fees are charged they are based on the patient's ability to pay.

In 1965 New York's state hospital system came under attack by Senator Robert F. Kennedy because it did not

provide adequate facilities for the mentally retarded. No
one would really argue that those facilities could not be
improved. There had been other scandals involving New
York state hospitals; there have always been scandals in
state hospitals, and there always would be as long as there
was too much demand and not enough money. New York's
advanced system, however, was being copied in 1965 by
other states, including New Jersey, which was undergoing
a thorough shakeup of its system.

Even as other states copied, the New York system was
changed for the better in 1965. The new program, which
became effective in the autumn, eliminated much of the
stigma from hospital admission for mental illness, thus
encouraging informal and voluntary admissions; it abol-
ished the "certification" of mental patients by judges and
placed admissions to state hospitals under medical control. It provided for reviews and safeguards, so that there
could be no "forgotten" patients in the New York system.

State hospitals were always notoriously good targets for
political investigations. For one thing, even in 1965, most
of them were antiquated and burdened by the inability
or the reluctance of the taxpayers to support them. In
Colorado in 1964 the state hospital in Pueblo lost part of
its accreditation from the Joint Commission on Accreditation of Hospitals because it could not meet the physical
standards established by hospital and medical experts. The
Democrats made a political complaint about this (the Republicans were then in control), just as the Republicans
had made a political issue of the state hospital during previous Democratic administrations. The matter of hospitalization became a political affair in spite of the fact that
an eight million dollar construction program then was in
progress. The Colorado state hospital had been neglected

for many, many years and only relatively recently had
serious efforts been made to meet the state's responsibilities to citizens who were mentally ill.

But Colorado should not be singled out for complaint.
In the spring of 1965, Texas was scandalized when a convicted murderer escaped from the San Antonio State Hospital with the assistance of a hospital employee. The up-
roar increased when it was discovered that goods had
been stolen from the hospital canteen, that patients were
given permission to drink in nearby bars, that at the Austin State Hospital sexual perversion was practiced by at
least one doctor. These scandals caused Governor John
Connally to seek new laws to govern mental institutions
in Texas. He asked the creation of a State Board of Mental Health and Retardation, made up of psychiatrists and
other physicians.

As the stories of New York State, Colorado, Texas, and
other state and local government hospitals show, at the
state and local level the public received just about the
kind of hospitalization it was willing to pay for and arrange through tax moneys and bonded support. When
Cook County Hospital in Chicago suffered a severe shortage of nurses in 1964 it solved the problem by raising the
pay scale.

In the 1960's the largest government hospital system in
the world was that of the Veterans Administration, with
115 hospitals. From very poor conditions of relatively few
years ago, the VA hospital system had developed into one
of the finest in the world. The secret had been a complete
reorganization during the Eisenhower Administration,
when General Omar N. Bradley was head of the Veterans
Administration.

When General Bradley came to office, the VA hospital

system was thoroughly confused. The VA hospitals were old, many of them were obsolete, and the concept of VA hospitalization was for the most part custodial, not aimed at treatment and rapid release.

By 1965 the picture had changed almost completely. Ninety-six of the VA hospitals, more than half of them, were affiliated with medical schools, either teaching medical students or serving as workshops for resident physicians affiliated with medical schools. The control of the medical facilities of the VA hospitals was vested in the Dean's Committees of various medical schools. Then, with recommendations of the Dean's Committees, and with government money to build what was necessary and to straighten out kinks, the responsibility for good medicine and good hospitalization was placed on the shoulders of the most advanced medical workers: the teachers. By 1966, VA hospitals with 35,000 beds were directly affiliated with teaching institutions, and an equal number had a more limited relationship under the control of the medical schools. Some 1,200 VA professional staff members, about a quarter of all VA doctors, had academic appointments at American colleges and universities.

Veterans Administration hospitals had improved more than any other group of hospitals in the decade that ended in 1965, or at least the improvement had been more spectacular. The VA hospital was no longer the gloomy spot it had once been. In spite of the red tape accompanying hospitalization in any government unit it had become a most humane institution. At the White River Junction Veterans Hospital in Vermont, a patient came in one day in 1965 suffering from a spinal disability. It was apparent that he would have to undergo extensive surgery and remain in the hospital for a considerable time. He was a farm

worker in central Vermont, not a wealthy man or he probably would not have been in a Veterans Hospital, although
a veteran need only show that he has a service-connected
disability and if hospitalization is indicated he must be
admitted within five days. If the disability is not service-
connected, the veteran may still enter the VA hospital if
he cannot afford private hospitalization, and the regulations on this point are subject to broad interpretation.

This particular Vermont veteran could not afford hospitalization elsewhere. Indeed he could afford practically
nothing. His wife and children were about to be evicted
from their home, and they had nowhere else to go. He had
no money to give them, nor could he earn any while he
was in the hospital. After hearing of their problem, John
O'Connell, administrative assistant to the chief of the medical staff, telephoned legal aid societies, the Red Cross,
the local post of the American Legion, and other organizations to secure money, legal help, and physical help for
the veteran's family. This service went even beyond what,
in hospital circles, is casually spoken of as TLC, or Tender
Loving Care.

Of course, there are also unpleasant stories about Veterans Hospitals. The largest malpractice awards of the
1960's have come in cases that involved Veterans Hospitals. Government hospitals, their mistakes and their problems, are seldom left unexposed to the public view for
very long.

When the Veterans Administration wanted to close
eleven of its hospitals in the spring of 1965 because of
rising costs and obsolescence, immediately there arose a
storm of protest from the American Legion and other
pressure groups, and from the Congressmen of the affected
areas. The VA had announced that by closing these insti-

tutions and spending money more wisely in more modern
hospitals it could save $23,000,000 and provide better
services. The public outcry was too great, however, and
in the end five of the hospitals were retained in service—
although nobody could argue that this represented good
hospitalization or good government.

One of the hospitals that was to be closed was the Grand
Junction Veterans Hospital in Colorado, a general hospital then serving 110 patients. It employed 219 persons at
an annual payroll of $1,183,000.

When the closing of the Grand Junction Veterans Hospital was announced in February, a Denver post of the American Legion began a campaign to defeat the plan. The commander of the Leyden-Chiles-Wickersham Post of the
Legion charged that the Denver Veterans Administration
Hospital could not handle the extra patients who would
come there if the Grand Junction Hospital were closed.
The director of the Denver Veterans Administration Hospital denied this and said that those who opposed the hospital closings were making exaggerated charges. The
Grand Junction Hospital, this official said, was suffering
from declining demand for its services. That being the
case, the VA could not afford, any more than any other
hospital organization could, to refurbish, maintain, and
bring up to date a dying institution.

The Leyden-Chiles-Wickersham Post of the American
Legion had been noted in the past for its outspoken defense of veterans rights and veterans welfare, as the Legion views these, and its officials began to send up a
barrage of press releases. "The Denver Veterans Administration Hospital is unable to take care of patients for whom
the Grand Junction Veterans Hospital was built," said
George H. Astler, the post commander. "As of this morn-

ing the American Legion was unable to procure admittance for the following patients: four neuropsychiatric, eight medical, and 12 surgical.

"While the Denver hospital lists vacancies, these are limited by classification, and if the patients for whom the Grand Junction Hospital was built do not come under the classification open in Denver they would have to remain at home or perhaps on top of one of our mountain passes.

"Right now a veteran is being forced from the Denver Veterans Administration Hospital on the ground that technically he should be in a nursing home."

The Legion post then recommended that the VA be forced to prove its ability to handle patients without using the Grand Junction Hospital.

The director of the Denver VA hospital reported threats and a telephone harassment campaign.

He charged that the Denver Legion Post had put many veterans up to applying for admission to hospitals although they were not in need of hospitalization, to put pressure on the VA. "They have gone out and shaken the bushes for these people," he said.

In Washington, during this argument, it was revealed that a special medical advisory group had recommended the closing of these eleven institutions. In every instance, said the chairman of this group, the doctors and other experts involved had agreed that the hospitals had outlived their usefulness and should be closed. Dr. Thomas H. Brem, Professor of Medicine at the University of Southern California School of Medicine had this to say about the changes:

"In the present instance, however, we are convinced that there will be many more instances of hardship re-

lieved than created, and that the over-all medical program
of the Veterans Administration will be rendered much
more effective in the services that it provides to our veterans."

With the spring came proliferation of political pressures
on the VA and on the Administration. Late in the spring
President Johnson announced that he had extended the
lives of five of the 11 hospitals, including the Grand Junction Hospital. It would be too much of a hardship, he
said, for the patients there to cross over the mountains to
go to Denver.

So the American Legion of Denver won its battle with
the Veterans Administration.

Nothing was wrong with the victory, except that the
good will of those medical and other professional men
who served the VA had been abused by this political operation. This is the way of American politics, and President Johnson could not be faulted for his manipulation of
what had become an intensely important political situation.

Elsewhere, in areas of hospital management not so re-
sponsive to political influence, some government hospitals
have taken drastic measures to cut costs in recent years.
Harry Payne, the administrator of Thomason General
(County) Hospital in El Paso, Texas, said one day in 1963
that he was determined to get his hospital out of the red
in its operations. What he meant, since this is a government hospital, was that he intended to make the hospital
live within its budget, which in 1963 was $1,700,000.

There had been talk in El Paso of getting rid of some of
the department heads and other key persons in the hospital and replacing them with less expensive personnel.
Others in El Paso thought that Payne could combine some

jobs, such as those of the business agent and the purchasing agent. Who needed a medical records librarian, when the position paid as high as $7,200 a year?

Payne retorted that if this particular hospital ever hoped to become accredited by the Joint Commission, the city fathers had best continue directing city political affairs and let him direct those of the hospital. Without a medical records librarian there was no chance that the hospital's medical records would be in good enough condition to make the hospital acceptable to the Accreditation Commission.

Thomason General's cost structure is not unlike that of many other hospitals. Most of the money goes for nursing services and hospital services. Less each year goes for the "hotel" service of bed and board.

Administrator Payne, in the 1960's, received $20,000 a year for running the hospital. Next in line in money was the director of nursing, who received $10,000 a year—and there Payne proposed to make a cut, for he regarded this salary as out of line with other administrative salaries. The business manager received $8,100, the medical records librarian was next; then came the pharmacists at $6,000; chief X-ray technician at $5,820, chief laboratory technician at the same; the purchasing agent at about $5,500; a personnel manager, a little lower; a physical therapist at $4,800, a dietician at $3,900 with an assistant who was paid $300 less; and an occupational therapist at about $3,900.

The pay of these people, plus that of all the kitchen personnel, cleaners, and those not directly involved in providing care to patients, went into the great catch-all of "hospital" costs. This was the area in which much of the seven to ten percent per year increase in hospitals' costs was found, and there were some very good reasons for this as well as some plainly inevitable ones, such as inflation and the constant American drive for betterment of economic position on all levels.

In that respect, however, there was absolutely no difference between the government hospital and any other variety in the United States.

Chapter Four

HOSPITALS
FOR PROFIT

The really unusual aspect of hospitalization in America in the second half of the twentieth century involves the continued existence of quite a different kind of hospital from all others: the proprietary hospital, which is run by doctors or others not for charity but for the express purpose of making a profit.

In recent years proprietary hospitals have declined in numbers in the United States, although the number of beds in these hospitals has increased in total, and so has the number of admissions.[1]

In 1966, by far the largest number of proprietary hospitals were in the 25-49 bed category, making them small hospitals. Most of these hospitals in this category were owned by corporations. The most beds were located in the 50-99 bed hospitals, also owned by corporations. There were 218 proprietary hospitals in the 25-49 category, with about 8,000 beds, and 209 hospitals in the 50-99 bed category, with 14,407 beds. There were only 76 corporate hospitals of the 100-199 bed category, but they contained nearly 10,000 beds.

The largest number of proprietary hospitals, about sixty percent of them, were owned by corporations. Some twenty percent were owned by partnerships, and another twenty percent by individuals. Seldom did individuals own really large hospitals, although two individually owned hospitals of the 200-299 bed category were listed in 1963 by the American Hospital Association. The largest proprietary hospital listed had more than 500 beds, and was owned by a corporation.

In terms of the total number of hospitals and admissions, the proprietary hospitals are very much in the minority. Fewer than fifteen percent of all short-term general hospitals are proprietary hospitals, and fewer than seven percent of all admissions came into those hospitals. And yet the proprietary hospitals of America in the 1960's caused more concern and trouble by far than their numbers or percentages of patients would indicate. If they could meet the standards of accreditation of the Joint Commission, if their charges were approved by the Blue Cross and other insurance companies, and if they were licensed by their states, then the operations and profits were the sole concern of the investors. Some health authorities believe that such a purely commercial system should not be permitted in hospitals. In fairness to proprietary hospitals, however, it must be said that among them are very good hospitals. The survival of the proprietary hospital in the 1960's is an indication of the failure of society to meet the needs of the country with more readily accepted forms of hospitals, as much as it is an indication of the survival of the profit-making system in health care.

The American Hospital Association divides the United

States into nine regions, trying thus to study the hospitals in terms of regional labor problems, wage rates, and other criteria.[2]

It is generally stated among hospital authorities that a major reason for the survival of proprietary hospitals has been rapid population growth. An argument can certainly be made in defense of this thesis. Two of the great growth areas of America in the years since the end of World War II have been Long Island, in the suburb area of New York, and California. New York state accounted in 1963 for sixty proprietary hospitals, or around six and a half percent of the total, and most of these were located either in New York City or in Nassau County, the county of Long Island closest to New York. In California there were 158 proprietary hospitals in 1963, or around seventeen percent of the total of proprietary hospitals, and by far the largest number were located in Southern California, the greatest growth area, with the largest concentration around Los Angeles.

Yet high population or even rapid growth was not necessarily linked so very closely to the strength of proprietary hospital systems. Two of the areas showing the greatest rate of growth in America in the years 1950-1960 were the new state of Alaska, and Nevada. Alaska's population increased 75.8 percent, from 128,643 to 226,167, yet in 1963 Alaska had *no* proprietary hospitals. Nevada's population increased from 160,083 to 285,278, and in 1963 Nevada had only three proprietary hospitals.

Another area of significant growth in this period was Florida, where population went from 2,771,305 to 4,951,-560. Florida, in 1963, was the home of twenty-one proprietary hospitals.

Population increase was a controlling factor in the

growth and survival of proprietary hospitals, certainly, but other reasons suggested themselves. The 14 states of the old Confederacy, plus certain border states, accounted for 522 of the nation's proprietary hospitals, or fifty-eight percent of the total.[3]

Two factors helped cause the strength of proprietary hospitals in the old South. One was the poverty of governments in the area, and their general backwardness in public health care. The other was racial discrimination.

In terms of proprietary hospitals this discrimination need not be overt. The social conditions under which a citizen seeks a private hospital apply largely to non-minorities, least to the colored minorities, for proprietary hospitalization exists almost entirely for the well-to-do in the United States. There are exceptions, in the cases of medical groups which own and operate their own small hospitals, but these exceptions are so rare as not to form any large part of the American hospital problem.

The United States is not alone. Throughout the world proprietary hospitals exist, totalling not more than five percent of total bed capacity. Everywhere these proprietary hospitals, sometimes called clinics and sometimes called nursing homes, exist for the wealthy who for one reason or another wish privacy and seclusion from the general public. In terms of total beds, the American percentage of proprietary hospitals is well within that figure.

Occasionally, as in Dallas, Texas, the rates of some proprietary hospitals are lower than those of the public hospitals. These rates should be consistently lower, because most proprietary hospitals give little or no community service in the form of emergency rooms, ambulances, teaching, out-patient clinics, or charity work. Nevertheless, in 1965 the American Hospital Association reported that the costs of the proprietary hospitals in America were the highest of all categories of hospitals.[4]

There are good proprietary hospitals and bad ones. The overall picture is troublesome enough that in several states the legislatures and health departments have begun to control them. Massachusetts, for example, looks very closely at proprietary hospitals through its state division of Hospital Facilities, which passes on applications for building permits. Connecticut watches them through its licensing procedure. New York limits hospital construction through careful screening.

In New York, an attorney for the Blue Cross made strong charges against proprietary hospitalization in pleading a court case which the Howard Park General Hospital brought against New York's Blue Cross organization when Blue Cross cancelled its service contract with the hospital.

Speaking of the proprietary hospitals, attorney Charles H. Tuttle said:

"They are organized for the profit of those who have the financial control and expect to receive returns. And, Your Honor will see at once that there is in that situation not only a conflict of interest, but a dangerous conflict of interest, between those who go into the matter of the hospital for profitable speculation on the one hand, the proper care of the patients, and also the amount of the cost bills which will go to the Blue Cross for payments.

"Your Honor will see at once that it is perfectly easy to deal with patients in such ways, for example, as having them stay in the hospital for two or three days more than they really need to stay there. There is the charge made for drugs and that sort of thing, which in the hands of one

who is seeking a personal profit can be very much affected
so that Blue Cross is confronted when it comes to the proprietary hospitals, with this situation."

J. Douglas Colman, chairman of the Board of New
York's Blue Cross, also went on record as opposing the
further expansion of proprietary hospitals in 1965. California maintains various regional advisory bodies. The
Illinois legislature, in the spring of 1965, considered legislation to stop the building of small proprietary hospitals
which were planned by investment syndicates, aimed at
making a "fast buck."

Something new has entered hospitalization in America,
and this is known as the "hot bed trade." Certain proprietary hospitals, called rackets by their critics, do not even
welcome really sick patients. Illinois State Senator Arthur
Gottschalk said that such hospitals overcharged patients,
sold laboratory, X-ray, and diagnostic services that were
never indicated by the medical reports on the patient, and
permitted inferior medical practices.

He charged that they showed "a high incidence of unnecessary appendectomies, hysterectomies, and tonsillec-
tomies." Some of these hospitals, in Chicago, were organized and financed by hoodlums. The former president of
one suburban Chicago hospital, a physician, was convicted
of counterfeiting $20 bills.

In Florida, a woman took her son to a proprietary hospital for an appendectomy. The mother and boy arrived
at about seven o'clock in the evening, and the eleven-year-
old boy was undressed, examined, and given medication.
Two hours later an employee of the hospital asked the
mother to take her boy to another hospital, because she
could not produce $200 in cash to guarantee the payment
of the hospital bill. She took him to another hospital in a

nearby city, where the operation was performed. Later she sued the proprietary hospital and won an award of $5,000 for the boy.

Another scandal, a serious one from the point of view of decent hospitals, occurred in California, early in the 1960's at a private hospital run for profit. This hospital was operated in connection with a medical group. It was a forty-bed hospital that operated during the late 1950's and until the summer of 1962. It was also a scandalous place, as the community learned in the autumn of that year when the hospital closed its doors and criminal charges were brought against the physician who controlled the hospital.

The doctor and three others were convicted of criminal conspiracy after a trial that lasted ten months, in which some ninety witnesses testified. In several thousands of pages of testimony, the witnesses reported the following abuses:

The office manager of this hospital was told to bill patients for reducing, setting, and casting fractures in spite of radiologists' reports showing no fractures.

Patients' hospital insurance accounts and patients themselves were billed for non-existent hospital visits by doctor.

The doctor's mother packed pills in envelopes in the clinic and bragged that she could do it blindfolded.

A young woman who went to the hospital for X-rays was insulted by the X-ray technician who made rude remarks and fingered her breast as he worked.

An unnecessary appendectomy was performed on one patient.

A patient was charged $200 for plastic surgery he never received.

X-rays were ordered on every patient, regardless of symptoms.

A young woman came into the hospital with a chest ailment and was told she needed pelvic surgery.

A hospital orderly sutured the wounds of patients and gave orders to nurses to give injections to patients.

A chiropractor testified that he was informed by a member of the hospital staff that the hospital gave kickbacks to doctors for sending patients there: one-third on medical cases, a half on surgical, and a half on obstetrical. He complained that he sent eight patients to the hospital and received nothing.

A nurse's aide testified that she was called on one day to administer anesthesia during an operation. The patient's breathing stopped, whereupon the anesthetist in charge gave oxygen and artificial respiration and brought the patient back to life.

Charts were changed, and non-medical personnel walked around the halls masquerading as doctors.

Small wonder that this hospital finally closed its doors. It was purchased later by another doctor for a price reportedly around $275,000, and reopened under another name as a legitimate hospital. By 1964 it was accredited by the joint commission and there was no fault to be found with it.

For the dishonest, doctors or not doctors, the proprietary hospital can offer a way to get rich quick. Too many unnecessary operations are still performed in this country, according to the best hospital administrators. Few are performed at voluntary or government hospitals. Many are performed at proprietary hospitals.

In New York City, in the survey of hospital care conducted by Columbia University and the Teamster's Union, it was apparent that more people were sent to the hospital unnecessarily in proprietary hospitals, that the quality of medical care was lower there than in city or voluntary hospitals, that more operations were performed there by unqualified surgeons, and that more unnecessary operations were performed in proprietary hospitals than in any other kind.

The statistics were surprising. As to admissions: in 67 cases studied in hospitals affiliated with medical schools, 63 of the admissions were agreed by the study group to have been necessary. Of hospitals that had teaching programs, but were not affiliated with medical schools, 157 admissions were studied, and 133 of these were believed to be necessary. Smaller voluntary hospitals had more unnecessary admissions, eight of 56 were unnecessary; in municipal hospitals all 27 cases were believed to be necessary; but in proprietary hospitals 26 of 99 admissions— more than a quarter of them—were not necessary.

In surgery, while the statistics for other hospitals were relatively the same, the figure of unnecessary operations in proprietary hospitals jumped. Of 105 admissions for surgery, the study group found that 32 were unnecessary. The highest figure of unnecessary operations and admissions was found among doctors who had no diplomas from specialty boards, were not fellows of the American College of Surgery or the American College of Physicians, and were not members of the staffs of either voluntary or municipal hospitals. These doctors, in other words, did all their surgery and hospitalization at proprietary hospitals.

Most of what the surveyors called "patient exploitation" occurred in proprietary hospitals. Many of these involved hysterectomies (removal of the reproductive organs of women). There were several cases involving Cesarean

births (delivery of babies by means of an abdominal operation) which were considered to be totally unnecessary.
In all hospitals, with heavy emphasis on the proprietaries,
the surveyors felt that one third of the hysterectomies and
more than one half of the Cesarean operations were unnecessary. Half the hysterectomies in proprietary hospitals
were unnecessary.

What this meant was that the best doctors do their operations in the voluntary hospitals. As the surveyors put
it: ". . . if patients select physicians with lesser qualifications they are more apt to be operated on in proprietary
institutions where the standards for physicians performing surgery are minimal or non-existent."

Many of New York City's proprietary hospitals were
badly planned and badly laid out. Some had not been designed as hospitals at all, and several were, in 1965, very
much out of date. Yet in the soaring values of the 1960's
they continued to be immensely profitable ventures. At
the end of World War II one of these proprietary hospitals
in New York was up for sale for $350,000. In 1965 that
same hospital, with very little alteration, sold for $3,500,-
000.

In 1965 the overall average of American hospital costs
on a daily basis was a little over $41, and that of the pro-
prietaries was $43. Where the state and federal, city and
voluntary hospitals' costs included large amounts for public service, the proprietary hospital's costs included profit
figures that were very often inflated.

In California, the proprietary hospitals which chose to
belong to the Southern California Hospital Council were
brought under control. One small hospital in Los Angeles
submitted to a study of seventy major surgical cases. The
total hospital charges, before figuring them on the council's

guiding basis, were nearly $400 for each operation. After-
ward the charges were about $50 less. The big cuts were
in laboratory fees, supplies, and drugs, for it is here that
hospitals can overcharge patients almost at will.

Elsewhere, proprietary hospitals were not nearly so well
controlled as in California. The Teamster's survey of 1965
shows that 53 percent of those who went to New York's
proprietary hospitals received substandard care, and 26
percent were hospitalized unnecessarily. This meant that
in such cases the entire hospital bill was an overcharge.

In Nassau county on Long Island, half the hospital
beds in the entire county in 1965 were located in proprietary hospitals, for the same reason that California had so
many—rapid growth. Proprietary hospitals in New York
grew so fast that they threatened the voluntary hospital
system.

The most objectionable aspect of the proprietaries from
the public point of view was the sometimes obnoxious
manner of their profit-taking. This was not true of all, but
it was true of enough that the general claim is not unfair.
Often high salaries are paid to the managers of these hospitals, chiefs of staff and others. High expense accounts
are run up. Rentals of property are paid to family corporations, thus increasing hidden profits. Pensions, life insurance premiums, and other expenses of the people who
own these hospitals are often charged to the expense of
the hospital, and thus are paid for by the patients. In a
series of articles in January, 1965, the New York *Herald
Tribune* revealed many unpleasant facts about the uses of
proprietary hospitals by their owners. Gift shops were run
by the family for the family's benefit, and of course, the
purchasers at such shops were led to believe that these
shops served a charitable purpose. (They were not dis-

abused of this idea.) Physicians sometimes operated the X-ray departments of these hospitals as "concessions," and paid for the privilege. They made it up in the sale of X-rays. Some doctors who own hospitals have been known to have their own pharmacies, too, and to prescribe for patients in code so that only these pharmacies might be used.

One hospital owner in New York travelled to Europe, and then charged it off, plus his wife's expenses, as the cost of doing business as a hospital owner. He was, he said, searching for a continental chef for his hospital.

The worst aspect of proprietary hospitals in the 1960's was the tendency of their owners to divest themselves of their capital investment by increasing the mortgages and other debts on the hospital's physical assets. This practice, which enables them to abandon the hospitals with very little loss, plus their methods of billing and charging, have brought may states to the point where they are now trying to stop the construction and licensing of proprietary hospitals.

Yet here is a positive side to the proprietary hospital story: in many communities doctors have banded together and pooled resources to build good hospitals and to operate them on the strictest principles of sound hospitalization. One such is Doctor's Hospital of Beverly Hills, which does public service and treats emergency cases.

Another useful proprietary hospital is The Dallas Medical and Surgical Clinic Hospital, a 25-bed hospital operated by a medical group of 33 partners. It has an emergency service—but only for its own clinic patients, not for the public. It is operated as a convenience for the doctors, who prefer to practice medicine in the clinic and visit their patients in their own hospital. It is operated for profit, but assistant business manager Arthur L. Cook said that the hospital makes no profit. Its room rates are lower than those of the larger Dallas community hospitals. It has only private rooms, which range from $20 to $30 per day in cost. Strangely enough, it could be much cheaper for a middle-income patient to be hospitalized at this proprietary hospital than to go into one of the big city or voluntary hospitals in Dallas. There *are* some excellent private profit-making hospitals. If the patient is careful he will get just what he is looking for.

Chapter Five

EXTENDED CARE—THE HOSPITAL
AND THE NURSING HOME

Nursing homes and hospitals for the chronically ill are becoming far more numerous and important in America than ever before with the passage in 1965 of the Medicare legislation, under which 19,000,000 of America's aged will be eligible for government-insured hospitalization.

Under the Medicare law every American over 65 is eligible for 90 days' stay in a hospital, and 100 days' stay in a nursing home, in any 250 day period. Actually, the pressure from all sides will be to move patients out of the "acute" hospitals quickly, and into nursing homes. All responsible government, medical, and hospital authorities agreed at the end of 1965 that the greatest immediate pressure under Medicare would be exerted on chronic-care facilities and nursing homes.

Until 1965 the American nursing-home business was an eyesore in the American social system. For every good nursing home, operated by registered nurses and licensed practical nurses in a clean, humane manner, there were two or three vile charnel houses, operated by greedy seekers of profit, who employed slatterns and mental deficients to care for the helpless. Many nursing homes stank of feces and urine and the odors of wasting disease. Almost everywhere in America the very word "nursing home" or "convalescent home" had an unpleasant connotation, and the good homes found it almost impossible to live down the reputation of the bad.

For two decades before 1965 the American Hospital Association had been trying to establish uniform standards for nursing homes. How far short most fell was shown by hospital checks, which indicated that of 70,000 American nursing homes, only 25,000 could meet standards that any professional organization called adequate, and in 1965, only 5,000 American nursing homes could meet the requirements of the Medicare program that would begin the following year.

In a few brief sentences the legislators who drew up the plans for Medicare set the stage for a major change in the American nursing-home business and for the first time made it possible to turn it from an unpleasant and often dishonest enterprise into a respectable and orderly affair.

Government did in short order what responsible hospitals and doctors had been trying to do for many years. Government did it by requiring that nursing homes become affiliated with responsible hospitals in order to qualify for payments under the Medicare program. The federal government would regulate the hospitals and the hospitals would regulate the nursing homes. Thus, for the first time in American history, beginning in 1966, Americans would enjoy national standards for nursing home care. The impact of this revolutionary change was bound to affect every community in the nation.

The Nursing Home Story, as one might call it, was a tale of hairbreadth escape by America from a tragedy which might have been brought about by the struggle of the American Medical Association against government participation in and backing of American health care.

The story begins in the 1950's, when hospitals became as concerned with the general American health problem as with their own specific problems. Nursing homes were like cesspools in the landscape. In order to free their beds for acutely ill patients, and in order to find places for the chronically ill and the aged in a society that was becoming ever more disoriented from family, the hospitals looked to nursing homes. When the administrators went to inspect these homes, too often they discovered charnel houses into which they could not consign their patients in good conscience.

The hospitals then, through the American Hospital Association, began a program to raise the standards of nursing homes. At first there was much resistance from the nursing-home owners, for nine-tenths of the nursing homes of America were proprietary institutions run for profit. Many were operated by doctors. Many were operated by nurses. Some were operated by school teachers and others who discovered this means of augmenting income. The nursing home was guaranteed a clientele because state and county and local governments had to have some place in which to keep the old and infirm who could not take care of themselves. Until 1965 most state government officials averted their eyes from the nursing homes, not wishing to accept responsibility for the filth and degradation into which they plunged the old and sick. Theoretically, nearly every state "regulated" the nursing homes.

Actually, the regulation was minute, as the low standards everywhere indicated.

Regulation of nursing homes was difficult because doctors had opposed regulation. Around 1960 the American Medical Association was persuaded to join with the American Hospital Association to attempt to work out a program of control. Elsewhere in this book the failure of that program is noted as an aspect of the general disagreement of doctors and hospitals about government participation in bringing American health care standards up to a high level.

After the 1963 split between AHA and AMA, each organization proceeded to move in a manner that was typical of its general public spirit. The American Medical Association set up a private program. It aligned itself with the American Nursing Home Association, which represented the proprietary nursing homes. The AMA position was that given the opportunity, the free-enterprise, profit-making nursing homes would and could police themselves. The fact that they had never done so through their own association did not seem to be a matter of vital concern to the AMA.

The American Hospital Association took quite a different approach. Its program, established in 1964, called on the nursing homes to accept accreditation and inspection, and to accept a supervisory relationship from a general hospital. This idea, of course, was anathema to the doctors; it was only proof to them of their public contention that the hospitals were trying to take over the control of health services in America.

In 1964 and early 1965 the American Medical Association and the hospitals showed that neither, alone, could do a very good job of standardizing nursing homes. There were not enough good homes to work with. In over a year only 1,000 homes could be found to meet standards established by either organization.

Then came Medicare, and with it the establishment of standards that were relatively as high as those of the American Hospital Association. The basis for control would not be free enterprise, as the doctors wanted, but orientation towards the needs of the community as the Hospital association wanted.

After its defeat on Medicare the AMA joined the American Hospital Association to recreate the system it had scorned a year and a half before. The nursing homes of America would be accredited by the Joint Commission, just as hospitals were, under standards to be established by the Joint Commission.

The first set of standards was published on October 2, 1965. It provided that: The nursing home or convalescent home must have been in operation for six months under the same authority. It must have a state license. It must provide information for the Joint Committee. Its ownership must be known. There must be no discrimination by race, color, creed, or national origin. The administrator must be qualified in health care. The home must use a recognized system of accounting, so that records could be readily examined. The home must keep proper insurance. Relatives must be informed of the patient's condition on a periodic basis, and immediately in emergencies. Physical plant and equipment must be adequate. A licensed physician must regularly care for the patient, seeing him at least once a month. The home must have a staff of two physicians for regular advice and consultation. The home must arrange for dental services when necessary. Provision must be made for laboratory and radiology services. The home must come under supervision of a hospital. The nursing service must be under supervision of a full-time registered nurse. Real medical records must be kept, to give history and other vital information needed by doctors and hospitals. Menus and diet must be controlled and records kept.

Before the regulations were published, the nursing home business suddenly began to burgeon as businessmen began to understand what Medicare would really mean in terms of money. Beginning in 1967 any aged person (over 65) could spend up to 100 days in a nursing home following each hospitalization and the government would guarantee most, if not all, the payment.

When Medicare was passed, lawyers all across America began drawing up incorporation papers as doctors and profit-making corporations laid plans to build nursing homes. The company that owned one motel chain announced formation of a new company to build 400 nursing homes in the next few years after 1965. This group said it would train and equip homes and license others to participate. Nursing homes, in other words, were to become a franchise operation like Dairy Queen and Carvel ice cream stands, or Howard Johnson Motels.

This was the most ambitious of hundreds of plans. Even in 1965 these plans were late in coming, at least in many parts of the country. Foreseeing the problem much earlier, doctors and others had already begun building nursing homes. In 1965, officials of the Iowa Department of Health warned investors not to buy stock in new nursing home ventures there. Those who did, said Iowa Hospital Director F. W. Pickworth, would be "in dire straits one of these days." In Iowa, nursing and custodial homes had increased their capacity by 150 percent in six years. Hospital Director Pickworth said nursing homes were being oversold as an investment.

Everywhere, investors were preparing. On Long Island a nursing home was opened with charges to begin at $85 a week for occupancy of a three-bed room, and rise to $135 for a private room. In New York City, construction began on a nursing home that would have 500 beds and rise seventeen stories. This would be a $6,000,000 project, and, of course, it would be a proprietary home.

Private operators hoped Medicare would bring a bonanza. To be sure, Medicare would guarantee payment of nursing home bills on a real cost basis, not on a per diem basis, as state and local governments so often paid. But by policing facilities the government might take much of the profit out of nursing homes.

Some professional nursing-home operators thought this the greatest danger. In New England, one such operator had been planning to build a three-stage care unit. He would supply bedrooms, cafeteria, dining and public rooms for old people in one wing. Next to this wing would be another—the central portion of the building—into which the old person would move when he became feeble and needed minimal care. Later, as he became more feeble and approached the "terminal" stage, he would be moved into a third unit, which would offer intensive nursing care. There he would die. All that was left out of this program were the services of an undertaker and a burial plot.

This nursing-home owner had made enough money, operating a nursing home with fewer than fifty beds for a decade, that he had no qualms about putting up a $250,-000 building and furnishing it. He was delaying, however, to see how Medicare worked out. He was very leery of regulation. He detested the Department of Health in his state, because its officials insisted on sending inspectors to examine and regulate his nursing home, and because the state taxed him. He was a firm advocate of free enterprise; he wanted no government interference. He was worried, he said, because Medicare threatened in 1965 to take the profit out of the nursing home business.

The nursing-home business had been intensely profitable, particularly for the unscrupulous, for many years, because there were no effective standards of care anywhere, and where state government did regulate nursing homes, the regulations were slipshod either in conception or in inspection.

Vermont, for example, inspected its nursing homes regularly, but the standards of care even in homes called good by doctors were never what the law demanded. "We all break the law," one registered nurse who owned a nursing home said cheerfully. How regularly and how seriously they broke the law meant the difference between high profits and only moderate profits from the operation of nursing homes.

The story is much the same in all fifty states. In Massachusetts in 1965, 29,000 patients occupied 727 nursing homes. Of these, 70 percent were welfare patients, their fees paid by county and state. (In one first-class home in Vermont the ratio was quite different. Of 39 patients, only 17 were welfare patients. This home was very profitable. Its proprietor did not like welfare patients, because government paid too little.) Massachusetts regulated its nursing home under the Nursing Home and Related Facilities Division of the Department of Health. The director, a physician, had the services of seventeen inspectors on his staff, but these had to inspect some five hundred rest homes and other facilities, as well as the nursing homes.

In 1965, Massachusetts closed down three nursing homes in one week in August. One was closed because the responsibility for the care of eighteen patients for twenty-four hours a day was placed on one elderly practical nurse. Another home was closed because patients had dirty feet and needed baths, there were flies in the kitchen, and the inspector discovered broken furniture and filth in the house. A third was closed because the plumbing did not work properly, the kitchen was filthy, and special diet patients were given regular meals. This home was also guilty of allowing patients to remain in their beds, covered with urine and feces.

These complaints could be matched in any American state in 1965. A California hospital worker said that she went one day to visit her mother in a nursing home and found her lying fully clothed in her bed between soiled sheets. The mother had not been given a change of clothes for several days.

In New York City in 1965, investigators checking several homes found indescribable filth in bathrooms, cockroaches in water pitchers, attendants who struck the patients, and attendants who refused to respond to simple requests because the patients had no money to tip them.

In a Chicago nursing home patients were discovered to be infested with lice, and of 200 nursing homes only ten percent were declared to be of reasonable quality by outside investigators.

One of the serious problems of nursing homes was the construction of the buildings. In the 1960's, most of these homes were old houses. They may have been built by wealthy families, but they were not built with fire alarm systems, fire extinguishers, dishwashing units, and adequate plumbing facilities to accommodate 20 to 50 people, or with uniform ceilings or uniform room construction. The fire hazard in many nursing homes was serious: early in the 1960's the National Fire Protection Association said that homes for the aged (and this included nursing homes) were first on its list of hazardous places in which to live.

In 1965 several new controls on nursing homes were brought into effect in various parts of the United States. In New York City authorities discovered that real estate operators had been quietly building proprietary nursing homes, often under guarantees by the Federal Housing Administration, which gave them 95 percent of the money. The real estate men were being touted into the business by bankers, and they in turn persuaded operators to undertake management of these proprietary homes. Bankers told investors that they might earn 25 to 30 percent of gross income in profit. (The only way so high a profit margin could be earned would be to advertise one standard of care and deliver a standard far inferior.)

New York put an end to this with legislation that brought state control to these proprietary institutions: no new hospital or nursing-home beds could be built without the approval of the New York State Hospital Planning and Review Council, and the Department of Health was given sole responsibility for planning the distribution of hospitals and nursing homes in the states.

Until the coming of Medicare, one limiting factor on control of nursing homes was public ignorance and apathy. In Vermont, where there were three classes of nursing homes, depending on the variety of care given, several nursing home operators said that in all their experience no patient or patient's family had ever asked about the classification system. In a third class nursing home, occupied largely by men, several of the patients had never in their lives consulted a doctor before they entered the home.

New York's law brought public attention to similar conditions in that state. In New York City, twenty-two nursing homes were forced to close down when the new code was passed. They reopened as residences or boarding houses. That is what they had really been all the time, although they had other pretensions. In many of the so-called "nursing homes" there was no responsibility at all for medical care for the ill, there were no nurses or practical nurses, and no supervision of the senile. Filth and terrible squalor were more the rule than the exception. Paul Screvane, President of the New York City Council, described these places as "houses of horror."

That was 1963. A year later they were gone, wiped out by regulations that could not be considered harsh by any standards, but they were regulations that forced nursing homes to provide the services they advertised.

The Joint Commission's requirement that nursing homes would have to be affiliated with hospitals was one of the finest controls possible on nursing-home care. Doctors and other members of the hospital staff could be counted on to pay frequent calls on these homes. Under such informal spot-checking, dishonesty, carelessness, and improper care could hardly continue to be the hazard they had been. Further, the Joint Commission would demand licensing from local authorities. This would insure frequent local examination for adherence to fire and safety rules. The rules would demand administrative supervision by a physician, not by a registered nurse as was often the case in 1965. They would demand the maintenance of good medical records, which very few nursing homes had in 1965. They would demand that the nursing homes avail themselves of diagnostic services of the hospitals, which meant that patients would be in little danger of developing new ailments which would be ignored. It would mean adhering to good dietary standards—which perhaps one nursing home in two did in 1965. (There was probably less cheating in the matter of food than in any other part of nursing home care in 1965. As one nursing-home operator explained: "about the only thing they have to look forward to all day long is the tray." This proprietor might break the rules regarding nursing and qualifications of workers, but he did not cheat on food, for that would have been bad business.)

Finally, and perhaps most important to the chronically ill among the nursing home patients, the homes would have to have trained nursing care available 24 hours a day. This regulation was in force only for the finest of nursing homes in 1965, and even there it was more honored in the breach than in observance.

Nursing homes, beginning in 1966, would be just as good as the Joint Commission on Accreditation would insist that they be, and even if the Joint Commission were to give the proprietors every leeway, the improvement would still be remarkable.

Nursing homes have often been used for the care of the chronically ill—those suffering from diseases such as chronic bronchitis, or a similar recurring and weakening disease—who need quite a different type of hospitalization or care than those with appendicitis or pneumonia. Until 1965, care of the chronically ill was given very much on a hit and miss basis; some of it was excellent, much of it was poor, and some was degrading to humanity. In 1965, with the passage of the Medicare law, the future for the chronically ill suddenly became bright.

Special hospitals for the chronically ill have existed in America for a long time. Sometimes they have been supported by fraternal and union organizations, such as the Pythians or the Printers' Union, which maintained homes for the aged and ill. Sometimes they have been an adjunct to the "county poor farm." Sometimes they have been state hospitals. For a very few there have always been the private and comparatively expensive sanitaria.

All this changed in 1965. After the passage of Medicare legislation, the chronic-disease hospitals, sanitaria, and nursing homes could look forward to an increased demand for care, and they began preparing for it.

For the established hospitals that deal with chronic disease, the change would mean a higher degree of occupancy, perhaps, but almost certainly an easier financial road. Government would help pay the cost on a realistic basis.

Many chronic disease hospitals in America are simply old hospitals that have passed their prime and can no longer meet the needs of the community. There is nothing wrong with this concept, for the chronically ill do not need the same level of care that the acutely ill need. But they do need cleanliness and personal care, and it is in these that such hospitals have been lagging.

A typical small chronic-disease hospital can be seen in the Guggenheimer Hospital of Lynchburg, Virginia, given to the city in 1914. It was an old white building, surrounded by spacious lawns, located nine blocks from downtown Lynchburg, and had been the residence of Max Guggenheimer, a prominent, public-spirited citizen. First it became a playground and park facility. Then, in 1931, it was made into a children's hospital. In 1944 it became a maternity hospital. In 1951, the old building was turned into a geriatric hospital, a non-profit community undertaking to care for the aged and infirm. In 1963 more than sixty old people were undergoing treatment there.

Such a mixed history is not unusual of hospitals for the chronically ill.

In New York City, a supervisor of nurses at the Bird S. Coler Memorial Hospital on Welfare Island complained that by her standards the patients at that hospital were very much neglected. Bird S. Coler is a chronic disease hospital of 1,900 beds, operated by the city of New York. The nursing supervisor reported that some psychiatric ward patients were left strapped in wheelchairs, without cushions, from morning until night. Some patients were slapped and pushed by attendants when they failed to respond as rapidly as desired. Once, a 101-year-old man argued with an attendant about sleeping in a bed with bars on the sides. The old man did not want to do so. After the centenarian was forcibly put into bed, and the attendant had left the room, the old man tried to climb over the bars, fell onto the floor, and sustained fatal injuries.

These are not atypical conditions in hospitals for the chronically ill.

Much has been learned in the last half of the twentieth century about care of the old and chronically ill. Some hospitals are leading the way in studies that will benefit millions of Americans in time. One such is the Montefiore Hospital in the Bronx, in New York City, a non-profit hospital which operates the Loeb Center for Nursing and Rehabilitation.

Montefiore Hospital's patient cost per day is $60, *not*

abnormal for general hospitals in New York City, but the daily cost in the Loeb chronic care center is only $30 per day. When a patient moves out of the acute stage of illness, but still needs hospital care, he may be moved from Montefiore into Loeb. The proposition is this:

Illness has two stages. First is the biological crisis, when the patient needs intensive medical and surgical services. This is called the "curing" stage. The nurse at this stage feeds, bathes, and cares for the toilet needs of the patient, administers medicines, and comforts him.

Then comes the second stage, what the people at Loeb call the "caring" stage. This stage is not recognized at ninety percent of acute treatment hospitals, and some concerned with chronic disease say that much "chronic illness" is directly attributable to the release of patients from an acute stage into an uncaring world.

The patients come to Loeb in the "caring" stage. The nurse works with the patient to bring him back into a normal world. At Loeb, the patients recovering from hip fractures are up and around in two or three months, about half the time that elderly people with hip fractures usually spend in recovering. One 82-year-old woman was admitted to the Loeb center as a wheel-chair case. She did not know where or who she was. She could not control her bladder or bowels. She was, some might have said, in an advanced stage of senility caused by the shock of fracturing her thigh. This woman went home, walking, in two months, in control of her toilet habits and herself.

Another woman, 78, was admitted after repeated hospitalizations for arteriosclerotic heart disease and irregular heart action. After a few months her symptoms had ceased and she was discharged. After nearly a year they had not returned.

Loeb's method of treatment was to comfort the patient, and teach him how to come back to normal. Each was given an examination, and then a plan was laid out for his recovery. Perhaps one of the secrets of Loeb's success was that the patient was informed of the plan, and was kept abreast of what was going on in his recovery program. If he wanted to talk to a nurse for an hour, he might. If he wanted to eat five times a day, he might make such arrangements, and he might use a special patient-kitchen to prepare snacks.

In 1965 this center for nursing and rehabilitation was operated very informally. The nurses did not even wear uniforms unless they felt like it. There were no "nursing stations." Wash basins and other devices were placed at a height usable for patients in wheel chairs.

Montefiore Hospital led the nation in another program that became doubly significant in 1965. This was its home-care program for the chronically ill.

Home care has been denigrated by doctors in some parts of the country because they worried lest it mean they would spend time running back and forth across their patient areas, making house calls. In an advanced program, such as Montefiore's, many of these calls were made by nurses and physical therapists.

Montefiore's program was really an extension of hospital care, and it may point the way to the future of hospitals as health centers.

Before home care and the Loeb center program began, many patients were discharged from Montefiore just as they were from other hospitals in America, to be forgotten by the hospital. Cardiac patients went away and never came back. They might suffer mild recurring symptoms, and they might do nothing about them until too late. No one encouraged them to come back for care. Only when such patients suffered dyspnea (painful breathing) would they call the doctor. It might then be too late.

After Montefiore started its program, the New York Blue Cross organization became interested and studied home care. It discovered that among 2,000 patients given home care, results were most encouraging.

Seventy-seven percent of these 2,000 people suffered from more than one disease. Most of them had circulatory disease, or cancer, or disease of the digestive system, and forty percent of them had undergone major surgery. Most of the people were between 55 and 74 years old.

First the hospital, where they were treated for the acute stage of the disease, then the Loeb center, where they learned to live with the disease, then home care, and finally family or self care—that was the beneficial pattern that emerged from such studies. It was effective enough that 14 of the 77 Blue Cross plans had adopted some form of home care program, covered by prepaid insurance, by the spring of 1965. Michigan had 35 hospitals working on a coordinated program; plans were in effect in Delaware, New Jersey, Wisconsin, and in big cities such as Philadelphia, Denver, and Boston. The idea was spreading as the nation became more conscious of the need to cure, and not just care for, its aged.

Chapter Six

THE HOSPITAL
AND THE DOCTOR

What is the relationship of patients to doctors, and patients to the hospitals in which they are given care? This is a very large part of the hospital crisis, for the relationship is changing all the time. The responsibility for many services that were once the province of individual physicians has now come into the hands of the hospital, sometimes with the acceptance and support of doctors, sometimes after the most bitter doctor-hospital warfare.

In this conflict one generalization might be made: those doctors with the highest sense of professionalism have accepted most of the changes, while those concerned with medicine primarily as a means of livelihood have not.

In the second half of the twentieth century, American health care has become so complex that in situations that require surgical procedures and advanced medical procedures it is impossible for any one doctor to do the job alone. In cardiology, radiology, pathology, anesthesiology, and other specialties, the expense of the machinery needed for these services is such that only a group practice or a hospital can afford them. Even here the hospital must be a large one to carry all the equipment and services on a full time basis. Some doctors have found the answer in group medicine and in clinics; another part of the answer is being found in the growing trend to make the community hospital the health center, particularly in the 429 hospitals in the United States which are affiliated with medical schools. There is also growing pressure across the nation for the creation of hospital medical centers.

These ideas raise complicated professional questions, involving the relationships of the doctor, the hospital, and the patient.

A comparison of two good hospitals in New England will show the best of the old and the best of the new approaches to hospitalization. They are the Rutland Hospital in Rutland, Vermont, and the Mary Hitchcock Memorial Hospital of Hanover, New Hampshire, roughly 50 miles apart. Both are hospital centers in predominantly rural areas, although Rutland Hospital also serves the industrial city of Rutland, with a population of 20,000, while Hanover, whose principal industry is Dartmouth College, is about a quarter as large.

Rutland Hospital is modern, built just a few years ago in an area several miles east of the smoky, noisy business section of the city. The new building replaced an old downtown hospital; a part of it is even newer—a new fifth floor was built in 1964.

Rutland is a community non-profit hospital which has been in existence for nearly three-quarters of a century. It operates on traditional hospital lines with a voluntary staff of doctors, and two specialist doctors on the paid administrative staff. It is controlled administratively by a board of public-spirited citizens, and medically by the independent physicians who *are* the staff, and who elect their own officers.

Early in 1964 the hospital was examined by the Joint Commission on the Accreditation of Hospitals and received compliments and a three year accreditation, the highest offered any hospital. The hospital conducts a school of X-ray technology, and this school and its facilities were examined by the American College of Radiology and approved for training. The hospital also conducts a program of nursing education in cooperation with Castleton State College, a few miles to the west. In every way Rutland Hospital meets the exacting standards of excellence required of a traditional hospital.

A Rutland citizen who falls ill enough to require hospitalization simply goes to the hospital, his doctor having reserved a bed for him. If he is well enough, he stops at the registration desk and discusses payment. If he is not well this will come later, for Rutland accepts all comers, then later asks about their ability to pay. In the hospital he is taken upstairs by an aide, shown where to put his clothes, and put into bed. His doctor, presumably, has telephoned the hospital, or is on the premises and gives the nurses instructions as to medication and special care, diet, or any necessary therapy. The patient is in the hands of his own family doctor, or of a specialist in the field in which he needs attention.

If the patient needs surgery, and his doctor is a general practitioner or a specialist in internal medicine, the doctor might perform the operation himself, or he might seek a surgeon's services. He would, in that case, recommend the surgeon to the patient and the patient would pay the surgeon's fees separately. If the services of other specialists are needed, these doctors also are brought to see the patient, and he pays their bills separately.

Rutland is not a large enough hospital to support interns and resident physicians. All the professional medical practice is carried out by the independent doctors of the staff, who instruct nurses and other professionals and service people in the care of the patient.

Mary Hitchcock Hospital, some seventy-five miles away in Hanover, represents what is sometimes called "team medicine," with the hospital serving not simply as a place for care for the patient, but as an integral part of the team's facilities. Mary Hitchcock's slogan is "teamwork for health."

Mary Hitchcock is called a Regional Medical Referral Center. Its nucleus is a 263-bed hospital, staffed by 65 members of a group-practice clinic. *No one else* may practice in that hospital. No one else may send a patient into that hospital. No one else may prescribe for a patient in that hospital. The doctors on the staff practice every medical specialty from anesthesiology (which Rutland Hospital does not offer as a hospital service) to dermatology.

The point is that a patient is not admitted to Mary Hitchcock Hospital by a single doctor, who then takes the *total* responsibility for his care. The patient is admitted, if he comes as a walking patient, after a visit with any one of the clinic doctors, and after his medical history is taken. He then has, at the call of his doctor, the services of specialists in all branches of medicine, without the usual charges of specialists. All the doctors at Hitchcock clinic are on salary. The bills received by the patient come from the hospital and the clinic, and they are inclined to be lower than those of patients who require specialty services in other types of hospitals. From the point of view of care, the important point is that this team medicine makes possible more facilities, more expensive equipment, and closer cooperation for the benefit of the patient.

In 1965 Mary Hitchcock Memorial Hospital also had the services of 45 resident physicians and 16 interns, and about 1,000 persons on the staff including members and employees of the clinic. It maintained training programs in nursing, medical technology, nurse anesthesia, X-ray, practical nursing, and the new specialty of hospital administration. It was the clinic of the Dartmouth Medical School. It was a center for research in cardiopulmonary studies, anesthesiology, neurosurgery, hematology, psychiatry, dermatology, and genetics.

To exemplify the importance of its team practice, the officials of Mary Hitchcock Hospital cite cases like this one:

"A young man with multiple serious injuries was admitted to the emergency room in critical condition after an automobile accident. He was in deep shock, unconscious, and had third-degree burns on 30 percent of his body. On the day following his injury he developed acute kidney failure. This patient initially spent several weeks in the intensive care unit, and through the team effort of several specialists in the hospital and medical school— neurosurgeons, urologists, a physiologist in kidney function, a plastic surgeon, and a physiatrist (specialist in physical medicine) he was able to walk out of the hospital unassisted a year later."

At Rutland Hospital a very personal relationship between patient and doctor is possible. When a doctor at, for example, nearby Fair Haven, Vermont, sends a patient to Rutland Hospital, he knows that patient inside out;

chances are that he may have brought the patient into the
world, for Fair Haven has doctors as close to the old-time
general practitioner who goes out into the stormy night as
any community in the country. Obviously there is a com-
forting factor in knowing your own doctor, a doctor who
has been treating you since you were a child.

There is another kind of comfort, too, and this is available at Mary Hitchcock Hospital. That is the comfort of
knowing that if you are having an operation, all the medical services will be in the hands of men and women who
are trained in the most modern developments of American
medicine, and will be available to you. In the years since
the end of World War II this has become far more important than before, because medicine has progressed so
rapidly that a doctor who does not study his literature and
keep up to date cannot practice truly modern medicine.
(This does not reflect on the small community doctor who
often does these things, too.)

It is obvious, then, that one of the problems in American hospital practice is the relationship between the patient and the health specialists, whether they be team
members, as they are in the teaching hospitals like Mary
Hitchcock, or individual physicians working together on
an unpaid staff in any given community hospital.

The decision cannot be made solely in favor of the
"team" medical practitioners. The question of doctor care
and doctors caring is not that easy to resolve. In the autumn of 1965, Dr. Carl A. Moyer, chief of surgery at the
Washington University School of Medicine in St. Louis,
resigned his position on the school faculty with a strong
speech against the practices of teaching hospitals and the
educational practices of medical schools.

As far as the patient was concerned, Dr. Moyer had

three criticisms: he said that it is nearly impossible to conduct well-controlled therapeutic investigations in teaching hospitals, that the clinical facilities in these hospitals were jumbled, and that clinics and hospitals under university control were becoming subject to internal dictatorship and special interests. He also criticized the growing importance of internal hospital politics and what he termed "Grantsmanship," the art of securing federal or foundation funds to carry on research projects. Doctors involved in these had a tendency to forget all about human beings in the hospitals they supervised, he said.

Too often, said Dr. Moyer, the professors in the medical schools let their interns and residents do all the work with patients, even their private patients. He charged that teaching doctors were becoming bureaucratic monsters.

In support of the community hospital, such as Rutland's, the American Medical Association began a program to make sure that the medical care Americans receive in the future would be far superior to that of 1965 in the smaller towns and cities. The move was toward specialization and finer medical education for all doctors. The medical school graduate did not go into practice after just a single year of internship in 1965. The American Medical Association had announced that within a few years even general practitioners would be required by the AMA to take three years of postgraduate training, while the estimated 80 percent of medical school graduates who would go into specialties must spend four or five years as residents in teaching hospitals to qualify. Then they must pass stiff examinations by one of the nineteen different specialty boards which have been formed by the AMA.

This program would bring changes for the better in American hospitals. The term "teaching hospital" would

soon be extended to hospitals that were not in 1965 parts
of university medical school complexes.[1]

Speaking of hospitals and doctors, Dr. Howard Craig,
Director of the New York Academy of Medicine, said:

"A great observer on the state of medical affairs, the late
Alan Gregg, once remarked that the hospital, instead of
being a place where a doctor saw a great many kinds of
patients, has become a place where the patient can see a
great many kinds of doctors."

The relationship among these doctors can be excellent
or it can be a disturbing factor in American health care.

For example, in 1952 in Ohio, a number of doctors established a clinic and medical group. They had the nucleus
of a practice in a prepaid group insurance program of the
United Mine Workers' Welfare and Retirement Fund.

The other doctors of this midwestern city showed the
entrenched attitudes that have generally marked the
American Medical Association. They did not like the idea
of group practice. They did not like the affiliation of the
group with the United Mine Workers. They reacted by
moving at a snail's pace in allowing members of the group
to join the county medical society. They controlled the
medical staff of the only hospital in town, and they were
not eager to allow these competitors to join the staff of
the hospital.

This discrimination against the doctors had an immediate and direct relationship to the welfare of patients of the
members of the group practice. Such a patient could not
enter the hospital unless he was admitted at the behest of
a non-group doctor, and once he was in the hospital the
group doctor could not treat him.

The members of the medical group sued the hospital

and the county medical society for several million dollars in damages. The suits were settled out of court. The doctors of the group were slowly taken into the "club."

The question here was whether the old-line doctors of this Ohio city were considering their professional responsibilities.

In New York state such problems became so serious that in 1963 the legislature passed a law prohibiting hospitals from discriminating against members of group medical practices in the granting of hospital privileges. The same type of law had to be brought into effect in Louisiana to stop medical ostracism that was hurting the public.

Another kind of discrimination among doctors has hurt American hospitals, too: this is racial discrimination.

Racial discrimination in hospitals has existed on several levels for many, many years but has been brought into the open in the civil liberties discussions of the 1960's. At the physicians' level examples can be found in nearly every community of the South, and they can also be found in New York City.

In 1965 Negroes had problems in securing medical education in New York, although not all these problems were the result of discriminatory practices by the medical profession or by hospitals. Hospital administrators in New York said the most important problem in securing more Negro doctors was to find Negroes who were qualified to attend medical schools. This meant Negroes must be given more opportunity at the lowest levels—and although this had begun in the 1960's it had not reached far enough to make a great difference at the medical school level—16 years away from first grade in grammar school. There was progress: by 1963 about 68 percent of the graduates of the two important American Negro Medical Schools, Howard and Menarry, were working in white hospitals as interns and residents.

Many of the best teaching hospitals claimed that they permitted no discriminatory practices. David Walsh, vice president of Memorial Hospital in New York City, said that his hospital had absolutely no discrimination in matters of employment or admissions.

On the level of graduate physicians and staff appointments to New York City's various hospitals, there can be little doubt that there was a kind of discrimination, even in 1965. A year earlier the New York State Advisory Committee on Civil Rights set out to find out just how much discrimination existed. The task was made difficult by the reluctance of New York hospitals to discuss the matter, even with a committee of doctors. Some hospitals cooperated. Some did not. Of the hospitals that did cooperate, 4,004 doctors were found to have admitting privileges. Of these 70, or 1.75 percent were Negroes, although Negroes made up 2.2 percent of the total force of physicians and surgeons in New York City. Negro physicians claimed there was definite prejudice in the matter of staff appointments. Where Negroes were admitted as staff doctors to hospitals it was mostly as pediatricians or anesthesiologists.

What did Negro doctors do in New York City? As elsewhere they practiced largely in Negro hospitals, or in clinics or nursing homes, or in other inferior "hospital" facilities.

In the winter of 1964-1965 this problem came to light when the State of New York's Department of Social Welfare ordered Mount Morris Park Hospital in Harlem to

stop caring for city charity patients because it had failed
to meet fire safety requirements.

What was Mount Morris? It was a 51-bed voluntary
hospital. It was built in 1920, not as a hospital, but as a
hotel. Later it became a private hospital and operated until 1948 as the X-ray Hospital. Then it became a community non-profit hospital, and in 1965 its 125-man staff of
physicians was almost entirely Negro. This was, in effect,
a Negro hospital.

When the Department of Social Welfare descended on
the hospital to enforce the law, Mount Morris's board
members appealed for mercy and for time to bring the
facilities up to government standards. "We are fighting for
principle," said Arthur Sinclair, chairman of the board of
the hospital, and a lawyer, "to give Negro doctors a place
to care for their patients."

There were very few such places in New York City, even
in enlightened 1965.

In the spring of 1965, Columbia University's School of
Public Health investigated hospitals in its city and dis-
closed the alarming facts mentioned earlier about doctors
and hospitals.

The Teamster's investigation of the cases of 400 patients
who were admitted to all kinds of New York hospitals
found that doctors played an important role in driving up
the cost of hospital insurance by putting people in the
hospital unnecessarily. In some of the New York hospitals
studied, four of every ten patients should not have been
there at all, the surveyors said.

The Teamster's Survey in New York also found that
poor medical care in that city was too often to be found
in the proprietary hospitals, many of them owned and

managed by doctors, and that these and the very small
voluntary hospitals had the highest incidence of unnecessary admissions.

The conclusion of the surveyors was that in New York
City, patients received the best hospital and medical care
at the big university teaching hospitals.

The Teamster's survey also showed that the best treatment in hospitals was given to patients by the doctors
with the best and longest training, which meant doctors
who had served as interns and residents for longer than
the usual time. However, these doctors often have a most
difficult time in their training years and some of their
practices—and the practices of hospitals—are not condu-
cive to good hospitalization. Take the story of one young
senior resident at Grady Memorial Hospital in Atlanta, Dr.
William J. Hardman, Jr. He was an obstetrical-gynecologi-
cal resident in a county hospital that is affiliated with
Emory University School of Medicine. He earned $325 a
month at his job. He was married and had two children,
and his monthly budget for living was $600. Where did
the rest come from? From what is called "medical moonlighting," a common practice among young doctors. Dr.
Hardman worked, in 1965, about 100 hours a week at the
hospital. After he had been relieved from his staff duties
(perhaps after a 30-hour stint) he would give physical examinations for insurance companies at a fee of perhaps
$10 for an hour and a half of work.

Other young resident doctors were known to cover calls
for private practitioners who did not want to take night
calls. In one midwestern city four resident physicians in
1964 formed a group moonlighting practice. They worked
for a pediatrician at night and on weekends. He paid them
$500 a month and a percentage of the fees for house calls

they made for him (and for which he collected his usual fee). Each man managed to earn an extra $250 a month from this outside practice.

Good medicine? Hospital administrators said it was not good medicine. The skilled pediatrician's calls were made by resident student doctors. The patients were not getting what they expected. The doctors were not getting the full fee. The doctor who owned the practice was getting much of it for simply owning the practice.

Good hospital practice? One hospital director put it this way:

"Moonlighting is not compatible with good graduate medical training. Our residents are on call at all times, and when they are off duty they are not relieved of their responsibility to their patients." Many hospital administrators were sympathetic to the young doctors who received so little pay for so much work, and in many areas moonlighting was winked at by doctors and hospitals, but others said that a young doctor who worked as much as 100 hours at the hospital had little time in a week for other activity, and that if he tried to burn the candle at both ends the result might be serious for an innocent patient.

Dr. Morris Fishbein considered this problem one day in his column in *Medical World News*. He noted that a survey made by the national magazine of residents, interns, and senior students, *RIIS*, showed that about a third of all residents and interns did moonlighting, and most of them because they were married and needed the money to make up for small salaries.[2] The problem, said Dr. Fishbein, was serious enough to call for the study of a medical commission, and that was his suggestion. In the face of growing demand for more training for doctors, this problem was bound to become more serious than ever, and unless hospitals meet the challenge and pay resident doctors and even interns more realistically, the service to the patients would suffer.[3] Resident physicians, as Dr. Fishbein noted, are no longer simply "extended students." They do diagnosis, medical treatment, and surgery.

One of the serious problems concerning doctors in the less conspicuous hospitals of New York City and other busy cities in 1965 involved the simple matter of a shortage of doctors, residents, and interns. More hospitals were accepted by the American Medical Association for intern and resident training than there were American-trained interns and residents to fill positions.[4] The result was that a fine teaching hospital like New York Hospital had its pick of the crop, while some other hospitals, even in New York City, must either go without enough interns and residents to do the work, or must employ young doctors from foreign countries with the promise of "training" them.

And perhaps the greatest problem of all for doctors and hospitals in the 1960's concerned the changing place of the doctor in American society. One problem was the increasing amount of the practice of medicine in hospitals. In 1963, 91,000,000 out-patient visits to hospitals for medical care were registered in hospitals belonging to the American Hospital Association. The number grew every year, and health authorities were confident that it would continue to grow.

Dr. Fishbein, in *Medical World News*, expressed concern from time to time about the problems of the physician in adapting himself to changing mores, and concern particularly with the physician's public image in America.

"The image of the individual doctor is often hurt by the failure of a patient to understand . . . the demands made

upon the doctor. . . . I have heard patients complain because the doctor would not make a house call at 2 a.m.,
yet the doctor might not have slept more than two or three
hours in the previous 48. I have heard patients complain
that they cannot get their doctor on a Wednesday afternoon in summer; yet Wednesday afternoon may be the
doctor's only recreation time all through the summer."

The doctor may not want what Dr. Fishbein calls "state-
medicine, socialized medicine, contract medicine, or sal-
aried employment." The AMA has been fighting these
trends with considerable vigor and success for the past
two decades. But the fact remained that the medical
practices of the nation were changing, and that the patient
who called his doctor at nine o'clock at night and did not
reach him might find a substitute for him, or might not,
unless in desperation he called a good hospital.

Chapter Seven

CONFLICTS IN
ADMINISTRATION

In the hospital crisis in America the physicians and surgeons in the 1960's were being faced with what might be a final choice: either step in and take responsibility for the operation of hospitals as health centers, or let non-medical bureaucracy take over and make the doctors into servants of the public in quite a different way than had ever been the case before.

Some doctors and lay hospital administrators said that doctors operate the hospitals of America and have always done so. In some places this was true. In some places it was not. The relationship between the non-medical hospital administrator and the medical profession was often strained; the administrator always walked on eggs when he dealt in certain areas of the hospital's problems, and the doctors justified ignoring many hospital problems by passing these unwanted headaches off as "business affairs." These same doctors were paying ever more attention to their own "business affairs," to the point where many

102

talked of what would once have been a disgraceful term
—"the business of medicine."

In 1964 Dr. Russell Nelson, president of Johns Hopkins
Hospital, warned doctors that they must go into the *management* of hospitals. Dr. Nelson, a physician, was involved in the administration of a hospital. So were many
other doctors, either as owner-administrators of their proprietary hospitals, or as directors and administrators of
government and voluntary hospitals. Some authorities
suggested that the administration of hospitals might become a medical specialty, forced by the expansion of medical services the hospital is called upon to perform in the
last years of the twentieth century.

Speaking before the American Hospital Association convention in 1965, Dr. Albert Snoke, director of Yale-New
Haven Hospital, one of the oldest and largest voluntary
institutions in America, discussed two grave weaknesses
in the voluntary health system in the United States:

"The first is the present uneasy relationship between
hospitals and organized medicine. The second is the lack
of recognition and proper utilization of those individuals
who are trained to meet the changing demands in health
care administration."

He warned that "we in hospitals are trying to run a mid-
twentieth century jet-propelled vehicle with a late nineteenth century steering system." The increasing size and
complexity of hospitals demanded full-time specialists in
hospital and health administration, Dr. Snoke said, not
plant superintendents. One serious problem was that administrative training in America for health care had not
caught up with the demands for administrators of health
programs, be they in health care, hospital construction
and rehabilitation, or medical research and education.

One of the problems was that the doctor, having under-gone four years of undergraduate college training, four years of medical school, a year or two as an intern, and perhaps a year or two as a resident, tended to look down upon the "administrator" as an inferior person, capable only of dealing in that nebulous pit called "business af-fairs." The fact, in 1965, was that the new crop of hospital and health administrators were men who had undergone four years of college education, three years of graduate education in hospital administration, and perhaps a period of "administrative residency" under programs such as that at Mary Hitchcock Hospital.

These administrators were truly specialists. In their own field they were as expert as the doctors in their fields. They would not expect to tell the doctor how to take out an appendix, but they would not expect the doctor to tell them how to achieve the most efficient use of a computer, either. Yet, instead of making partners of the trained ad-ministrators, and even adopting administrative medicine as a truly medical specialty, too often the doctors were fighting the administrators.

It was of more than minor significance, perhaps, that among the leading hospital administrators in the United States in 1965, those in most of the largest and best-run hospitals were not only administrators, but physicians. These men, like Dr. Snoke, spoke with authority. The M.D. after their names gave them that authority more than the title "director" did, whether they liked it or not.

The extent of the problem was outlined by Dr. Snoke:

"A challenge also is presented to the medical profession. Organized medicine needs to understand the commonality of purpose and goals of the hospitals and physicians and the need for strengthening and for preserving that which

is good in our voluntary health system as well as adjusting
to the legitimate public needs of today and tomorrow. The
medical administrator—be he M.D. or Mr., is the partner
—not the enemy—of the physician in this approach. However, he cannot be an effective partner of the physician if
he is not accepted. As long as physicians consider the
specialists in administration as automatically suspect—
there can be little progress."

If the doctors did not move into the hospital field they
were going to be displaced, the iconoclastic Dr. Carl
Moyer indicated as he resigned from Washington University School of Medicine in St. Louis. He noted the growing
supply of eager, restless, and very competent executive
talent in this country, men itching to get their hands into
social problems:

"The forced early retirement of corporation executives,
generals, admirals and surgeons-general, before their su-
perannuation, places upon the volunteer, and low-pay executive market, a group of highly intelligent, still ener-
getic, dictatorial organization men who jump at the chance
of again exercising their imperial talents in a way that is
ego-supporting if nothing else."

Dr. Moyer was referring specifically to administration
positions, hospital board positions, university positions,
and various governmental divisions which dealt with hospitals and medical education.

Another administrative problem in hospitals concerns
the casual manner in which the medical profession has
treated the subject of medical administration.

The voluntary community hospital with which most
Americans are concerned has three major authoritative divisions. At the top is the board of directors or governors or
trustees—whatever the group happens to be called. This

is the chief policy-making body in terms of overall, long-range community planning. This body determines building programs, sets social relationships with the community, and controls finances.

Next is the administrator, who functions much as does the president of a corporation. He makes sure that the hospital runs properly as a hospital and health center, providing services to the patients and public.

Third is the medical staff, which is responsible for the medical management of the hospital. No one would think of making a popularity contest of the election of board members of a hospital; the responsibilities are too great. No one would think of making a popularity contest of the selection of an administrator; the work is too hard and the responsibilities are too great. But the chief medical administrators of hospitals, the chiefs of staff, are very often elected on a popularity basis, or on the basis of longevity and political power in the county medical society.

As Johns Hopkins's Dr. Nelson put it, the position of medical chief of staff in a hospital is a management job, and "it shouldn't be at the mercy of the election of the least effective individual."

In any given American hospital the organization of the medical staff was likely to be the *least* effective organization in the hospital, not the most effective as it should be. For one reason, the hospital administrator usually had little control over this staff. There was a historical reason, too: the traditional control of American medicine by county medical societies. There was also a growing tendency to move away from this control, particularly with the emergence of strong group medical practice. One illustration was the Palo Alto Medical Clinic of California, a group practice of 95 doctors who treated 1,500 patients daily. The Palo Alto Clinic was rich and powerful, after 35 years in practice and was, in 1965, well along into its second generation of doctors. It pioneered, and helped provide funds for, the replacement of Palo Alto's fire-trap hospital back in 1930; it had helped all along with the growth of the community's Palo Alto-Stanford Hospital Center to a 440-bed institution.

In many areas there was still much friction in 1965 between doctors who were wedded to the old individual-physician concept and a new breed of medical men who believed in group practice. Not all doctors who preferred to practice alone were old fogies, nor was there any tendency on the part of hospital or even responsible clinic leaders to denigrate the general practitioner. The pressure, where it existed in 1965, was still all the other way around, it was the general practitioner and the individual doctor fighting against the changes of the twentieth century.

The story of the group in Ohio was a case in point: the Group Health Association of America gave $5,000 to these group doctors to fight their case. And what was the Group Health Association? It was, in a way, the group doctors' answer to the American Medical Association, which long ago approved group practice in theory, but whose local county associations often were found to be fighting group medicine.

This struggle was vital and very personal to labor unions and large associations, because at some time these associations or unions might decide to go into prepaid medical and hospital planning. This means total medical care, and perhaps hospital care as well, in return for advance payments. The patient would be affected because the medical societies often moved to keep doctors who participated in these plans from the staffs of hospitals.

In Pennsylvania, one county medical society fought a group of such doctors for a number of years. In 1964 the group had still made little success in getting hospital staff privileges.

The Pennsylvania struggle was much like the Ohio struggle: the entrenched forces of the old medicine were fighting the new. The doctors of the hospital in Pennsylvania claimed that the group doctors wanted to set up a hospital within a hospital. "Why should a dictatorial third party tell us what to do?" asked the hospital president. He referred to the United Mine Workers Union, which for its time inaugurated the most socially advanced hospital program in America, in connection with a clinic program.

This stemmed from the United Mine Workers Welfare and Retirement Fund, created in 1947. The UMW sent investigators into the mining areas of Pennsylvania, Tennessee, Kentucky, and West Virginia to see how their members were faring medically. They discovered that doctors in these poor regions of what America was later to discover as a blighted Appalachia, were indeed poor, and poorly equipped, just like their region. Few local doctors used modern methods or had modern equipment, there were practically no specialists outside the cities, and few hospitals could be classed as good.

Pennsylvania and Ohio were found to have an adequate number of hospitals. In the other areas not enough beds existed, so the Mine Workers built their own hospitals—10 hospitals with a total of 1,000 beds. These were built and staffed by 1956. The Mine Workers fund also inaugurated training programs for practical nurses, for medical technicians, and for registered nurses and nurse-anesthetists. The hospitals were sold in 1964 to the Board of Missions of the Presbyterian Church and after that time were operated as community hospitals.

As Dr. Howard A. Rusk wrote in 1964, "since the medical care program was established in 1948 more than three million miners and their wives have received good care in good hospitals for the first time in their lives. Before the program started, 31 miners' babies out of every 1,000 died. Now, less than 18 die and maternal deaths have been halved to one for each 1,000 births."

Still, organized medicine fought that program all the way, just as the AMA opposed Medicare. In the passage of the Medicare bill in the spring of 1965, for the first time in history the American Medical Association suffered a major defeat. Only near the end of the struggle did the AMA come up with an alternative to Medicare, but it was too late. Even Dr. Fishbein had reluctantly concluded, in January, 1965, that some government program should be inaugurated for the aged in America. It was not too late for the aged, but it was late for the doctors to direct the program. What they had feared most—government medicine—was to become a reality in the summer of 1966. How it would work out remained to be seen, but it was certain that how government medicine, or any kind of modern medicine, would succeed depended in large part on the attitudes of the doctors.

With what health leaders called "technical advances," [1] the lines of difference between university or teaching hospitals and community hospitals would disappear. Better medicine was already coming to the community hospitals in the training young doctors received, whether they were planning to practice in Rutland, Vermont, or in New York City.

By 1965 the American Hospital Association, which regulated the practices of the hospitals of America, had spent four years studying the problems of management of hospitals, to establish new management standards. Hospitals would be accredited in the future also on the basis of management and service to the community. In 1964 the AHA House of Delegates approved 16 principles, leading in this direction, the major one being that hospitals, all hospitals, are community enterprises. This philosophy has begun to trickle down in government, too, with public health administrators and courts making decisions that bring private and public hospitals closer together. Proprietary hospitals in particular were coming under closer scrutiny than ever before.

New York City in 1963 and 1964 developed a new hospital code to cover proprietary hospitals. This was the responsibility of the city government, for under New York law the state took responsibility for the standards of voluntary hospitals, but not those of New York City's 39 private hospitals, with their 5,310 beds. The new standards demanded that doctors seeking staff privileges at the hospitals be approved by a credentials committee, and that these hospitals run for profit maintain emergency rooms and treat all who needed emergency treatment, regardless of their ability to pay.

The matter of staff privileges for doctors in all hospitals was under survey by the courts in 1964. In the 1960's doctors were becoming more willing to take their grievances to court. Courts held that some hospitals, public ones in particular, might not exclude doctors from staff privileges without good reason. The courts in Missouri forced hospi-

tals to open doors to osteopaths; the attorney general of
Michigan in 1963 held that hospitals should be open to
any representatives of the healing arts who were licensed
by the state. Colorado, Florida, Texas, and West Virginia
specifically excluded osteopaths from hospitals, but California went the opposite way in combining osteopathy
with medicine.

A common fear among doctors is that politics will rear
its ugly head when government steps into hospitalization,
and this has sometimes been given credence by events in
public hospitals. In 1964 in Jersey City, New Jersey, the
mayor discharged the director of surgery at the Jersey
City Medical Center and appointed a surgeon who was a
friend of a local Democratic party leader.

The old director of surgery was past retirement age at
that time, to be sure, and the mayor did have the right to
make the appointment. The question raised was over the
process of selection. Critics said the job should have been
filled after discussion with medical leaders.

In New York City, the commissioner of hospitals in
1964 suspended the 42 member board of directors of City
Hospital in Elmhurst, Queens. The commissioner then
was Dr. Ray E. Trussell. He also dismissed the hospital's
medical director, Dr. Lester R. Tuchman, because he objected to the commissioner's plan to affiliate city hospitals
with teaching institutions, in this case Mt. Sinai Hospital.
Up to that time the commissioner had linked nine city
hospitals with medical schools. The commissioner was
upheld by the courts.

This was a most complex and difficult problem. It was
instructive to the public in one way: where hospitals are
controlled by government agencies, the final decision of
hospital policy may be made in the courts. It would not

seem that this is a very effective way to run hospitals, but it might be, as events progressed, that the courts would be called upon more and more to rule on hospital problems.

In Denver, a dispute between municipal and medical school authorities in the 1960's came close to destroying the effectiveness of Denver General Hospital. In 1947 a formal contract of agreement had been made between the Denver Board of Health and the University of Colorado Medical School, under which the hospital and the medical school shared facilities. In 1961 the Denver Board of Health ended the agreement, charging that the medical school was trying to run Denver General Hospital. By 1965 the dispute was still not settled, and city and medical school authorities were charging one another with the responsibility. The problem there was to determine who was in charge. City authorities demanded control of their own hospital, and the medical school authorities demanded control of medical school students and medical school personnel in the hospital.

Another problem arose in Denver in 1965, involving the Colorado General Hospital. In October of that year the regents of the University of Colorado asked the legislature for $600,000 more than the state legislature had allocated for the hospital for the fiscal year. (The university regents govern this university hospital.) A budget committee of the legislature recommended that only a little more than $200,000 be given the hospital. The regents then planned to close down thirty of the hospital's 288 beds, to eliminate 80 nurses and other hospital workers, and to reduce various services of the hospital. Dr. John J. Conger, vice president for medical affairs at the University, had originally asked the legislature for $8,200,000 to run the hospital, and had informed the budget committee that the original allocation of $7,500,000 was too small. The hospital's costs were rising more rapidly than its ability to adjust rates, although it had raised its rates from $28 to $30 for multi-bed rooms, and from $33 to $35 for single bed rooms.

The tragedy, from the public point of view, was that Colorado General Hospital was a new hospital, constructed at a cost of $18,000,000 to replace an obsolete building. One reason for building the new hospital was to increase the number of beds for public use, and this was done, but the beds could not be used if the hospital did not have the money to operate. Faced with budgetary problems, the hospital administration chose to cut back the number of beds and services to the public rather than compromise the quality of hospital care.

Another dispute about control of the hospital occurred at a community hospital in Connecticut, serving a small town that in recent years has become the home of many workers in a busy complex of factories. It is an old town, and for many years its doctors have been a homogenous group, general practitioners who took care of the current generation just as they had of the last.

A few years ago the hospital employed a young administrator who, with the apparent backing of his board of trustees, sought to make improvements. He wanted the services of some of the specialty groups which had begun to play an important part in medicine. In this attempt to encourage specialists in his community, the young administrator ran afoul of the county medical society and his own medical staff of general practitioners who resented

the idea of specialists coming to town, and further resented the idea that the administrator would bring them
in.

Gradually it became noticeable that this hospital, which
had been nearly fully occupied as were all hospitals, was
suffering from a decline in traffic. Many beds were empty.
As the days went on more beds became empty, and it did
not take long for the administrator, his board, and his staff
to realize that they were facing a doctors' strike.

The board and the administrator took no action for
some time, and the general practitioners continued to
send their patients out of the community to hospitals
nearby, and sometimes not so nearby. Finally the young
administrator could feel the tension growing in his board
of trustees, and when the hospital's bed use fell almost to
zero, he resigned rather than have the hospital destroyed
by this struggle. The chief nurse took over as temporary
administrator, and the young administrator went off to
better himself considerably in a new position.

The chief nurse functioned as administrator for several
months. The doctors slowly began bringing their patients
back to the hospital. But in a way the young administrator
had won his battle by the summer of 1965. The hospital
then had many services uncommon for a small hospital.
It had the service of a radiologist who came daily to read
the X-rays. It had its own pharmacist. The hospital was
used by specialists, and an obstetrician and gynecologist
came part time to serve the community. In the autumn of
1965, the hospital had the services of an anesthesiologist,
too.

One of the serious problems of hospital-doctor relationships has to do with four important and controversial specialties: radiology, pathology, anestheseology, and physi-

cal medicine. The principle is the same for all of them: they are specialties which are needed in a hospital and which, generally speaking, cannot be practiced outside a hospital. It is true that a radiologist might take X-rays and use ray treatment and radium treatment on patients outside a hospital and this is done. But the modern facilities for this work are so expensive that relatively few physicians could ever afford to equip themselves in this field, and if they could do so once, changes come so rapidly that it would be difficult for them to keep up to date.

Among American hospitals, about 3,400 (49 percent) maintain pathology laboratories. More than 6,500 (95 percent) offer diagnostic X-ray services, but only 2,100 (31 percent) maintain therapeutic X-ray services. 972 hospitals (14.2 percent) maintain rehabilitation units, of which physiatry is a part.

The facilities for pathology—good laboratory equipment and trained technicians—and the facilities for anesthesiology—various anesthetic machines and the anesthetics themselves—can best be housed in a hospital. The anesthesiologist, even more than the other specialists named, belongs in the operating room of the hospital and has only teaching and minor functions outside that room.

From the point of view of a hospital, these services were essential. From the point of view of the physician practicing these specialties, the hospital was his natural environment.

Consequently, as these specialties became more commonly practiced, and at the same time more complex and expensive for the practitioners, hospitals and the specialists tended to find grounds for cooperation. The hospital often took the position that it would buy and maintain all the equipment and place this equipment at the disposal of the doctor. The doctor would receive a salary and/or commission, usually quite high, for his work and for exercising his specialty at the hospital. He also might teach nurses and technicians.

All was well, except that the American Medical Association and some of the specialty group organizations took the position that these argreements put the hospitals into the practice of medicine, and created unethical situations. The point was: how should the patient pay for the services rendered him by these specialists in the hospital? Should the hospital collect from the patient, as a part of the hospital bill, and then give the doctor a commission, or should it pay the doctor in the form of a regular salary without reference to the number of patients he treated? Or should the doctor bill the patients himself? And if he was to use the hospital's equipment, then who was to pay for the equipment?

In 1965, in framing the Medicare law, Congress listened to the pleas of the specialty organizations and the AMA, and specifically said in the law that these specialists must bill patients themselves. If the law remained unchanged, hospitals and doctors would have to go through many circumlocutions and changes.

The associations of the various specialists indicated that they were willing to make any adjustments necessary in order to place themselves on what they called a truly "professional" footing. They had long felt inferior to other members of the medical profession because of the manner in which they were compensated for their services. After the Medicare law was passed, the radiologists and the anesthesiologists indicated at their annual meetings their intent to maintain independence from hospitals in billing.

The intensity of their feeling is well illustrated in the case of Dr. Lloyd Mousel.

Early in the 1950's, Dr. Lloyd H. Mousel was director of anesthesia at Swedish Hospital in Seattle. He filed a complaint against the Washington Society of Anesthesiologists and the King County Medical Society for "conspiring" against him.

Dr. Mousel had been paid a salary by the hospital for teaching, administration of the department of anesthesiology, and for the administration of anesthetics to patients undergoing operations in Swedish Hospital.

The doctors of Seattle objected to Dr. Mousel's "unprofessional conduct." For several years Dr. Mousel has been subjected to a campaign of what he called harassment. He was boycotted by Seattle doctors. His wife was snubbed by their wives. He was barred from the various medical societies to which he sought admission.

Dr. Mousel's lawyers put it this way:

"His professional and personal reputation and character have been damaged; this damage has been very extensive, but it is of such a nature as not to be susceptible to definite calculation in monetary terms. The plaintiff has been subject to professional and social ostracism. He has been subjected regularly to humiliation and mental suffering and embarrassment among physicians, plaintiff's friends, acquaintances, patients, and members of the public. He has been seriously hindered in the pursuit of his profession. His employment at the Swedish Hospital has been placed in jeopardy. If plaintiff loses this position, he has been placed in serious danger of being unable to secure employment at any other hospital in Seattle or anywhere else in the United States. . . ."

The Mousel case never came to trial. The unfavorable national publicity it received began to bother Seattle's doctors. Dr. Mousel changed the way in which he was paid by Swedish Hospital; instead of taking a salary and a percentage of charges for administering anesthesia from the hospital, he asked to be paid a salary for teaching and administration, which are not medical matters, and he billed patients directly for the anesthetics he administered.

In essence, Dr. Mousel retreated. The issue remained unresolved. For a time it seemed that it would be resolved early in the 1960's, when the AMA and the American Hospital Association were enjoying a period of compatability. The AMA then indicated that it saw no reason that doctors and hospitals could not work out their own arrangements on these specialties without interference from outsiders. But later the AMA and the AHA fell out, and the AMA reversed its field. The American Society of Anesthesiologists had long insisted that its members should be just as "professional" as other doctors, which meant that they should charge individually for anesthesia services.

In view of the increased need for men who could set up and direct and operate laboratories as pathologists, treatment centers as radiologists, surgical procedures as anesthesiologists, and physical medicine departments as physiatrists, the difficulty arising between medical specialists and the hospitals of the country created problems and will create more.

In December, 1965, Dr. Victor Buhler, outgoing president of the American College of Pathologists, warned that hospitals were attempting to amend the Medicare law so that hospitals could bill for pathology. (The law as passed in 1965 said otherwise.) The pathologists took the position that all laboratory tests included work by the physician, and so should be billed separately.

"I predict that we as pathologists and physicians will be involved in legislative battles for years to come," Dr. Buhler said.[2]

Important as the specialist issue was to the public, far more important was the reason for which medical association and hospital association embarked on the struggle in the 1960's over the future of American health care.

The AMA and the AHA disagreed basically over the question of federal assistance to hospitals and medical schools, and over the form of federal aid in the health field. The AMA did not always object to government assistance. Since the 1940's, half the hospital construction in the United States had been financed under the Hill-Burton Act, which was government support of health care. Most doctors had come to accept it, although some doctors opposed even Hill-Burton as a "foot in the door."

Doctors were not nearly so much of a mind about the Kerr-Mills bill, which was passed in 1960. Kerr-Mills provided that the federal government would contribute between 50% and 80% of the cost of hospital care for the poor. The program was to be administered by the states, but it was still "socialized medicine" for the poor. Many doctors objected violently to it.

The medical profession fell out, however, in 1963 over the King-Anderson bill, the forerunner of Medicare, which would provide for medical, surgical, and hospital care for the aged.

In the winter and spring of 1964 doctors and hospital men went to Washington to testify about the need or lack of need for such federal assistance. The doctors became suspicious of the hospital men and accused them of turning to support socialized medicine, whereupon the dispute broke into open battle. The King-Anderson bill was defeated, but in the election year of 1964 Medicare gave President Johnson a strong issue, which he used fully. After his landslide victory, the question of Medicare was resolved favorably, although it was not settled for another year. By the same stroke the framework of cooperation between medical men and hospital men, built slowly over many years, was suddenly destroyed. The question of specialists and their relationships to hospitals again became an issue.

In the summer of 1965, instead of yielding to the election returns, or offering a palatable substitute, the AMA continued to fight Medicare along the old lines. Congressmen listened to the doctors in Washington. They also listened to doctors who were hospital administrators, and to other hospital doctors. The AMA found that it could no longer claim to speak monolithically as the guardian of the nation's health.

The dispute between doctors and hospitals that broke out over Medicare became a problem for both in the question of hospital and nursing home standards.

The argument began in 1963 after the AMA and the AHA appointed commissioners to establish conditions and regulations for accreditation of nursing homes in America. Responsible proprietors of nursing homes wanted such accreditation. Through the state associations, they had been seeking approval by the hospital people for a number of years. In the past decade hospitals and doctors had begun to see how the nursing home *must* become the extension of the hospital, since costs were rising so high and hospital beds were so scarce that patients must be moved into and out of hospitals quickly.

The nursing home matter was proceeding in a reasonable atmosphere of amity, and doctors and hospital representatives were in agreement on most questions. Then doctors raised objections to the hospital attitudes toward socialized medicine or government medicine, and in a very short time the AMA House of Delegates voted not to cooperate with the AHA on nursing home accreditation.

The rift between the AMA and the AHA was one of the greatest of all threats to American health in the 1960's. How it would be resolved remained to be seen, even after the passage of the Medicare bill. Responsible leaders of the American Medical Association realized they had gone too far, and they made overtures to the hospital men. Responsible leaders of the American Hospital Association replied in much the same language, and it seemed that the breach would be mended.

Dr. James Z. Appel, the 1965 president of the AMA, appeared at the hospital convention in San Francisco and talked about peace. He also issued a warning:

"Doctors believe they do not render hospital service; we render medical service," he said, but he called for hospital and doctor groups to settle their differences by negotiation, before the federal government stepped in and established standards.

The AMA had never quit fighting against government control and initiative in medical matters. The AHA had given up the fight some years before, when it had become apparent that hospitals were rapidly going downhill because they could not keep up with the costs of construction to meet medical advances. With the cost of patient care rising as it did in the 1950's and 1960's, very few hospitals had money to sink into building funds. In the 1960's the Kennedy and Johnson administrations decided that even the Hill-Burton program was not enough, that the demand of the American people was for better medical care on all levels, and that the hospitals, which were being asked to provide that care, were not going to be able to manage it unassisted.

So there remained a difference in philosophy between the doctors and those who must face the problems of operating hospitals.

Late in 1965, AMA President Appel and the AMA leaders showed a willingness for reconciliation with the government and hospital leaders. At the final meeting of the House of Delegates in 1965 even the most sturdy opponents of Medicare showed a conciliatory attitude.

It was apparent to all by the beginning of 1966 that Medicare was only the beginning of a new look in American health care. The 89th Congress in one session had passed fifteen laws relating to public health, more measures and more important ones than had been enacted by any Congress during the previous decade. Medicare was the most important of these. The Fogarty-McNamara bill authorized a new program of community projects for the aged. The Fallon-Randolph bill provided for construction of health and medical facilities in economically depressed areas.

A bill backed by Senator Hill and Representative Harris authorized mortgage insurance and direct loans to encourage group practice of medicine and dentistry.

Another bill extended the Fair Labor Standards Act to hospitals, bringing the minimum-wage law into action there for the first time. Still another provided federal funds for medical schools, operating funds as well as loans for students and construction funds. The controversial

Public Law 89-239, which established regional medical centers for research and treatment in the fields of heart disease, cancer, and stroke, was also passed.

By the end of 1965 the trend in American health care was very clear. Political leaders saw a need for federal intervention and assistance and were acting on that basis.

Chapter Eight

THE
NURSE

In making a statistical analysis of hospitals the American Hospital Association does not use a category called "nurses" but instead uses the term "professional care of patients." The wording is significant; it reflects a change in the practice of what we know as "nursing." The professional registered nurse in the 1960's has become the leader of a nursing team.

Shortages of trained professionals, the high cost of maintaining registered nurses on hospital staffs, and the changing techniques of hospitalization have brought about this basic change in the nursing function. After the doctor, the registered nurse stands next in the line of professional authority and responsibility. Then comes the practical nurse, then the nurse's aide, and then attendants whose duties are extremely various. In the 7,000 American hospitals there are some 900,000 full-time members of the professional care teams, plus another 170,000 part-time nurses, practical nurses, and aides.

Asked to name the most serious problem facing hospitals, most administrators mention costs and nursing shortages in the same breath.[1]

The nursing problem is largely a hospital problem, because 65 percent of American registered nurses work in hospitals, nursing homes, or clinics. There are more than 600,000 of these professional people in the United States. One of the most serious problems is their concentration in a few areas. In 1961, for example, there were only half as many nurses for a given number of patients in California as there were in Connecticut. California has moved since then to close the gap, which was created largely by the huge growth of population in a very short time.

In the 1960's California suffered seriously from growing pains in the health field. Connecticut still had more nurses per capita in 1965 because Connecticut, with its population of 2,500,000, maintained 19 professional nursing schools, while California, with its 15,700,000 population, maintained only 20 schools. In 1961, members of the California Nursing Association said that seventy-five percent of the nurses practicing in that state had been trained in one of the other states of the Union.

Altogether, the United States had 875 hospital-controlled professional nursing schools in 1965, as reported by the National League for Nursing. In addition there were about 200 practical nursing schools controlled by hospitals. These were not all the schools where nursing was taught, by far, but those figures represented the approved schools, which in 1965 were training 95,000 students.

In that year the House of Representatives subcommittee on Public Health and Safety studied the nursing question, decided that 300,000 more nurses should be brought into the American health program by 1970, and recommended a massive construction program to build new nursing schools.

Mrs. Margaret Dolan, President of the American Nurses Association, backed this program. She also called for college training of more nurses. The American Medical Association supported the federal aid plan, too. The American Hospital Association opposed it, for Dr. James T. Howell of the AHA said that between 1951 and 1962, in spite of the shortage of nurses, 205 nursing schools closed their doors.

There are several varieties of nursing schools, and Dr. Howell's objection to the increase in hospital-controlled schools was based on the position shared by many hospital administrators: the cost of education in the health services should be borne by the entire community, and not by hospitals. Support by hospitals meant support only by patients and insurance-premium payers.

The three varieties of professional nursing schools are the college or university school, which requires four years of education and grants a bachelor's degree; the diploma program, which involves three years of training; and the associate program which involves two years. In all programs the student works for some period in a hospital.

The shortage of nurses exists on every level in the United States, for only about 30,000 are graduating every year, where health experts have indicated a need for 53,-000 a year. Testifying before the House subcommittee in 1965, Boisfeuillet Jones, special assistant to the Secretary of Health, Education, and Welfare, said that twenty percent of all nursing positions in the United States were unfilled as of that moment.

In terms of the Medicare law, the shortage could be

extremely serious, because the Joint Commission on Hospital Accreditation standards for nursing homes call for full-time supervision by practical nurses, and in 1965 one in ten nursing homes had no full-time professional nurse, or even a full-time practical nurse.

In terms of the best of hospitals, sometimes the shortage could be serious, too: in 1966 Miami's James M. Jackson Memorial Hospital was 100 nurses short, to serve its 1,218 beds; smaller Florida hospitals reported a chronic shortage of nurses.

The nurse shortage was being met in 1966 by various methods in various states. Doctor's Hospital in Coral Gables, Florida, reported that it was hiring "per diem" registered nurses—women who did not want to work full time.

The state of Oklahoma in 1964 found one way to ease the shortage of nurses. Oklahoma then had 4,000 active registered nurses but needed another 2,600 to supply the needs of hospitals and other institutions. Oklahoma had eleven schools of nursing, but they could not provide enough graduates in time to meet the growing problem. So the University of Oklahoma and the state nursing organizations began a program to bring back to service nurses who had married or "retired" for one reason or another. The key was a refresher program for registered nurses, conducted by *other nurses* in their local communities. The nurses being "refreshed" would go to school days or evenings for 60 to 120 hours, and on graduation would be given certificates of training. Oklahoma discovered that 80 percent of these "retrainees" took jobs at hospitals, in public health, or with doctors—and they stayed on the jobs. Oklahoma solved its pressing problem.

In New York City the large hospitals never had too

much trouble finding nurses. They paid well, and working
in a hospital such as New York Hospital or Mount Sinai
lent prestige to the nurse. The small hospitals had more
difficulty, even in the larger cities, but their problems
were not so very serious either. It was in the rural areas,
in the twenty-, thirty-, and forty-bed hospitals, where the
nurses had many responsibilities, that the shortage was
acute. The problem was most acute in areas where there
were no large population centers, for here it is difficult
to support the training of nurses, and once they were
trained it was difficult to keep them from migrating to the
big cities where pay was higher and life was more exciting.
Another problem was that most nurses married, perhaps
almost as soon as they completed their training. In past
years a married nurse, in the process of raising a family,
was considered as lost to the nursing profession, but times
are changing. All across the United States a determined
effort was made in the 1960's to attract more girls to nursing and to train nurses for the growing needs of hospitals
that are becoming larger, more modern, and more satisfactory places for skilled persons to work, and to bring back
to nursing trained nurses whose families were grown.
Even in less populated areas, such as Vermont, there is no
shortage of nurses in the population centers. Rutland Hospital, with its 235 beds, has no problem. In 1965 nurses
there started at $80 a week, and might rise to $94.60 for a
forty-hour week.[2]

The rate of pay for nurses across the state in the Mary
Hitchcock Hospital in Hanover was a bit higher, for Mary
Hitchcock had wanted to make sure that it would have
no labor problems, particularly in the skilled technical and
professional fields, and so it has been paying its nurses and

technicians at close to Boston rates, about ten percent
higher, for a number of years.

Discrimination sometimes has been a serious problem
in the question of nursing. However, recently nursing has
offered Negro women and women of other minority
groups (men, too, to a much smaller degree) one of the
few outlets for respectable, professional employment that
was accepted by a white society. This has been true for a
dozen years.

Twenty-five years ago it was not true. The New York
State Advisory Committee on Civil Rights found that in
1941 and 1942 there were few Negro nurses in voluntary
hospitals. But changes in medicine and hospitalization
have been enormous since World War II, and changes in
racial matters have followed. The Lincoln School of Nursing, established to create opportunity for Negroes who
wished to study nursing, was dissolved because it was no
longer necessary. Negroes were admitted freely to the
various schools of nursing in New York City if they could
qualify, and more could qualify in the 1960's than ever
before.

The National Negro Nursing Association was disbanded
in 1951, and its members were absorbed into the American
Nurses Association.

In the South the pattern was different. In many areas
Negroes have been thoroughly discouraged from seeking
nursing positions: in the early 1950's Parkland hospital in
Dallas discharged all its Negro nurses. Only in the 1960's
had the South begun to change.

James A. Hamilton, of a Minneapolis consulting firm,
surveyed health and hospital problems in Dallas in 1964
and reported that in 1965 Dallas would need 1,100 more

nurses and technicians than it was likely to have. The
city's four schools of nursing were graduating 145 nurses
a year, but this was not enough. Further, he said, Dallas
would be short 4,600 nurses by 1985 unless something serious was done to alleviate the shortage. The provision of
nurses suddenly loomed ahead as the greatest health care
problem in Dallas, greater even than the provision of the
additional hospitals beds that the city needed.

Shreveport, Louisiana, found itself in much the same
situation in the spring of 1964. Marie Prim, the director
of nursing at Northwestern School of Nursing in Shreveport, decided that she must resign. She and four other
members of the nursing faculty of twelve found it much
too difficult to go on with limited salaries and limited
budget. Shreveport had one of the poorest reputations in
the state where the pay and working conditions of nurses
were concerned: it was third from the bottom in salaries,
and it offered no rotation of hours or days for nursing supervisors.

Shreveport was already suffering a nursing shortage.
With the twin-city suburb of Bossier City, Shreveport's
population for the nursing area came to 200,000, and in
this there was a shortage of 100 registered nurses. Serious?
Dr. John A. Hendrick of the Conference Memorial Medical Center said this:

"Less than thirty-four persons could receive special
around-the-clock nursing at this time."

The problems of Northwestern School of Nursing, then,
affected every citizen in Shreveport and the surrounding
countryside.

Northwestern had been founded in 1950, by the consoli-
dation of the nursing schools of the five major Shreveport
hospitals. It was a four-year nursing school that gave a

college degree. It also had once used a diploma plan,
which involved 36 months of school and hospital training.
This plan had been dropped, but in 1964 there was talk
of reviving it to speed the process of training nurses for
northwest Louisiana.

Why was Shreveport having so much trouble in securing nurses and nurse trainees? Chiefly because the salary
for registered nurses in Shreveport averaged $283 a
month (compared to, for example, nearly $400 for nurses
in the even smaller city of Rutland, Vermont). In all Louisiana only Ruston and Thibodaux paid less. The average
pay for nurses in Louisiana in 1964 was $305.

Faced with this knowledge of low pay in the state and
even lower pay for Shreveport's area, local girls were los-
ing interest in the nursing profession. In 1959, Northwestern School of Nursing graduated eighty nurses; in 1960,
the school graduated seventy-five nurses; in 1961, only
seventy-four nurses; in 1962, only fifty-nine. In 1964, the
director of the school resigned.

At the same time, nursing affairs were improving in
Lynchburg, Virginia, because Lynchburg had already begun to do something about its problem. The Virginia State
Board of Nurse Examiners approved a one-year program
which the Lynchburg General Hospital had suggested as
a solution for part of its problem of patient care. In the
previous five years Lynchburg General had shown the
greatest growth of any hospital in the city. It was also
the only hospital in the city to serve all races.

While Lynchburg General's ratio of use had risen
sharply in the past five years, the increase in cost-of-pa-
tient-per-day was reported by the Virginia Council on
Uniform Hospital Accounting to be the lowest in that industrial city. That seemed excellent, but it represented

Lynchburg's nursing problem in 1963. Its three non-profit hospitals employed 850 persons in all, there were 128 physicians serving the staffs of those hospitals, and only 150 registered nurses. The ratio of nurses to doctors was very low.

When the problem of patient care became serious the administration at Lynchburg General sought remedies. First they inaugurated a one-year plan to train practical nurses who could take on some of the chores. These trainees would begin by paying a fee of $70, which separated the faithful from the curious. (It also created some hardship for the low income groups, which included the Negroes.) The money came back if the trainee was serious, for at the end of the sixteenth week the trainee would begin to receive pay of $20 a month. The school was not free, far from it. The students had to maintain themselves, although the hospital provided uniforms and laundry service and meals while they were at the hospital. The program involved 500 hours of classwork, with forty hours each week of training and practical work. The plan was open to all races.

In a sense nurses are the heart of any hospital. The symbol of Florence Nightingale still inspired many a girl to seek a career in nursing. But nursing in the 1960's is not what it was.

Those who like to look back sigh wistfully for the good old days when the nurse took care of the patient in a tender, loving manner. If the nurse did, and some really did do this, she was with the patient all day long, every day, seven days a week, until his discharge from the hospital. If the patient required round-the-clock nursing, he might have three such nurses, seven days a week. In the 1960's there was no such care; it would have been quite impossible in any hospital in the face of wage and hour laws, overtime restrictions, and just plain cost. The need for constant care during the critical hours in a patient's illness was answered in different ways. One way, as found at Memorial Hospital in New York City, was to put a patient into the Intensive Care section, which meant 24-hour-a-day nursing and constant watchfulness by all the staff. This was a ward situation, in some hospitals it meant four beds or more. At Memorial, the hospital cost was $62 per day in 1965. That was about half of what it would cost for a patient to have three shifts of nurses, each working eight hours to serve him, to say nothing of the cost of a private room.

In a survey of hospitals, administrators were asked if they accepted the complaint that hospitals had become "depersonalized" in the 1960's. Generally speaking, the administrators said hospitals *had* become depersonalized, and one of the primary reasons for it was the changed relationship of nurses and nursing to the patients.

This was not to accuse the nurses of having become hard-hearted. The mushy-hearted Edith Cavell can only serve within the framework of the accepted rules of her profession. Those rules, and the nurse's responsibilities, had changed markedly in the past dozen years.

For one thing the function of all hospitals had changed in thirty years, from a care function to a cure function. "Tender Loving Care" was going the way of all individual attention, the administrator of an up-state New York hospital said.

"There is no question that hospitals are becoming more and more depersonalized," he said. "You are admitted to a room, taken to the operating room, then to the recovery room, then to the intensive care unit. You then, as a patient, go into the regular care section of the hospital, and then into the convalescent section. This can happen in a week.

"You have a medication nurse, supervisors, head nurse, practical nurse, and aides. Instead of a nurse on 12 hours she is on eight hours five days a week. You are not a patient long enough to become acquainted with the personnel."

Further, said this administrator, life was going to become still more complex. Visiting a large hospital, he found that he had to speak to five persons before finding the department he wanted.

Nurses in 1965 felt strongly about the complaint that they are somehow failing to do their job, and that it was their fault that hospitals were becoming depersonalized. As one nurse pointed out, a student in any school might graduate with a ninety percent average and be considered a very good student indeed. But a student who made ten percent error in a hospital could not be kept on as a student nurse. "How does one make people 100 percent perfect?" she asked. That was the problem of the nurse (and the hospital). And why, asked another nurse, were the nurses always blamed when a patient fell out of bed? "If someone falls out of bed at home, nobody gets blamed. If a nurse forgets to give a dose of medicine to a patient, the world hears about it, but if a mother forgets to give a dose of medicine to her child who knows or cares?"

These were nurse's complaints, looked at from the nurse's point of view.

Small hospitals did not have so much of a depersonalization problem in 1965. An administrator from Wyoming said that in his small hospital "more time for each patient is granted, where in large hospitals the patient gets the care he needs and that's all."

That claim was not necessarily accurate, for some of the finest care is given in very large hospitals, while some small hospitals were so short of nursing personnel that only minimum care was possible. One method of increasing the personal quotient in relationship to patients was the use of nurses' aides, either volunteer Candy Stripers, Gray Ladies, or whatever they might be called, or paid nurses' aides, who did some of the menial tasks to leave nurses free for their purely professional duties.

Volunteers were very helpful in hospitals where their services could be properly used. In Memorial Hospital in New York City, volunteer workers made decorations for parties and gave parties for patients. At Halloween, 1965, some 150 ambulatory patients attended such a party, and the volunteers looked forward to it as much as the patients.

In 1965 there were ten volunteers at Memorial Sloan-Kettering Cancer Center who had been working for that hospital, without a penny of payment, for twenty years or more. Almost twice as many had worked voluntarily for fifteen years, 70 people for ten years; 150 for five years or more, and perhaps five hundred men and women who had a year or more of service as volunteers. Memorial Sloan-Kettering was a prestige hospital, and those who volunteered there had the satisfaction of working in a desperate situation. They said they could feel the drama of the fight against one of America's two most hated killers. But other hospitals that encouraged volunteers did not have much trouble in securing them. There were scores and hundreds of well-meaning men and women in every community who wanted to help the unfortunate. Among the growing leisure class of the retired there was a large volunteer labor corps.

But many hospitals, such as Rutland Hospital, did not want to be bothered with volunteer workers. Some hospitals only allowed them to operate a gift shop, or to run mobile trucks around the convalescent department handing out library books. These were services, but they were not the kind of services for which the hospital had great need.

One reason for the reluctance to use volunteer help in some hospitals was the fear on the part of hospital administrators and boards that malpractice suits might result from accidents involving these untrained, non-professional people. (Such people in fact need not be untrained, although they might be amateur, as hospitals which have established volunteer programs have discovered.)

The care of sick children in hospitals is an art in itself. For the child who goes in at night and has his tonsils out in the morning and is home the following morning, there was not much of a problem in 1965. It was a somewhat frightening experience, but most hospitals put the "tonsils" all in one ward and the children ate ice cream and sometimes played games together.

But for really sick children the nursing problem was serious. Some hospitals solved it by letting mothers stay with their children. For the very rich, who took private rooms or suites, this was not a problem. Other parents and other hospitals could take a leaf, perhaps, from the book of the Boston Floating Hospital. In one program tried there in 1964, the mother of the sick child actually lived in the hospital with him and took care of him, cooking his meals in a little kitchen, bathing him, and doing his laundry. She did everything but give professional medical and nursing service. All the mother's attention was supervised by the nursing staff of the hospital, but it was the mother, and not a stranger, helping the child.

How strong is the motivation of professional nurses in the 1960's was a question sometimes asked by disillusioned hospital administrators. One Oregon hospital administrator suggested that nurses be screened at school for their motivation at least as much as for their academic background. He said that he had considerable difficulty in keeping qualified nurses.

One way of strengthening the nursing in hospitals and at the same time putting the nurses on their professional mettle was suggested by Dr. Glen R. Leymaster, associate director of the American Medical Association Department of Medical Education in 1963. He proposed at a Virginia meeting that a new profession be brought into hospitals, a group which would stand above nurses, but below doctors in professional skills, a group to relieve physicians of some of their routine chores and allow them to give more attention to medical affairs.[3]

That tendency sounded more "depersonalizing" than personalizing, but it was matched by the activity of a voluntary hospital in northern New Hampshire, a 34-bed hospital that had begun the use of a volunteer "patient-relations coordinator." This volunteer spent time with the patients in this little hospital, giving them the feeling that somebody was basically concerned with their feelings as well as their symptoms.

At a twenty-five bed Montana hospital the coffee break was expanded, in 1965, to include the patients (unless their medical program forbade it). Volunteer nurses' aides made a specialty of "doing" the hair of the women patients who were well enough to appreciate the service. There was no complaint about depersonalization in that hospital.

St. Joseph's Hospital in Breese, Illinois, was building a new building in 1965. One of this hospital's prime considerations was to keep the nursing units small, "to enable nursing personnel to spend time with patients." The size of this behemoth which recognized the primary problem of care? Forty-two beds.

One of the technological developments that has made nursing more efficient is "team nursing." It also has the effect of giving the patient the impression that he is a matter of concern to everyone in the hospital.

At Waterbury Hospital in Connecticut this program was put into effect in 1965 in the hospital's Whittemore Nursing Division, which consisted of single and semi-private rooms and four-bed wards. In all, there were facilities for 28 patients in this division, and usually it was filled nearly to capacity.

Two nursing teams were established under control of the hospital's head nurse. A team consisted of a registered nurse, licensed practical nurses, trained aides, ward aides, orderlies, and ward clerks. Each team was responsible for fourteen patients. The registered nurse, or nurses if more were needed, took care of the sickest first, and sent those of lesser skills to do lesser tasks. Thus the patient was given good attention, the lights on the call buttons were watched, and there was no long hiatus between the patient's call for help and the staff's response.

At New York Hospital in the spring of 1965 a Coronary Care Unit was opened to provide better supervision for patients who suffered heart attacks. The idea followed a medical discovery; doctors learned that even if a heart stops beating, if they could get to it in time they could

often save the patient, without damage to the heart or to
the brain from anoxia (lack of oxygen). Time was the ab-
solute; it would be three minutes between the moment the
heart stopped and the moment that irreversible damage
was done to the brain.

New York Hospital put four beds in a ward or pavilion,
and one single bed in a private room, and hooked these to
an electronic network around a central nursing station.
The patients were linked to machines which monitored
their heart action at all times, as a nurse watched on TV
viewing screens. Each bedside had an automatic signaling
device which operated if the patient's heart rate exceeded
or fell below a predetermined range.

Fifteen registered nurses and practical nurses were
brought to work in this special unit under a nurse who
was a cardiac specialist. This highly trained staff would
be responsible for split-second action and decisions. All
this was new because medical skill had only recently come
to the point where it could save the medically dead.

The increase in medical and hospital technical skills,
then, can be seen as a basic factor in depersonalization of
nursing in America. Are any Americans willing to trade
back again?

Chapter Nine

LABOR

When the question of labor in American hospitals was raised in the 1960's it referred to a very general group of workers, most of whom had been seriously underpaid until 1965 when the federal minimum-wage laws were invoked by a new law passed by Congress.[1] The term "labor" in the 1960's did not generally mean the front-office, or administrative, employees. It certainly did not apply to the professional staff of doctors, nurses, and other skilled persons. Considering the laboratories and other special areas of the hospital, some workers were considered "labor" and others were considered professionals. Sometimes the line was fairly thinly drawn. Labor, in the hospital sense, referred to the housekeeping employees, dietary department employees, and a large mass of miscellaneous workers of various skills.[2]

The concept of "labor," and particularly of organized labor, in hospitals was relatively new. Where labor had been organized (and this was a very small and very spotty

140

portion of hospital labor in 1966) it had been organized
by several different unions. One of these was the Teamster's union, which in the years since World War II had
undertaken hospital labor organization because no one
else was doing it. Another was Local 1199 of the Drug
and Hospital Workers' Union, an association with 24,500
members that is an offshoot of the Retail Clerks' Union
and was founded for the same reason. There were other
unions in the Middle West and Far West. There was no
monolithic hospital labor union; in New York City in the
fall of 1965 some 21,000 employees of the municipal hospitals voted in an NLRB-sponsored election to affiliate
with the federation of state and local government employees.

One trend was apparent in hospitals in the 1960's, and
that was a slow movement towards the organization of
labor. Hospital administrators of the eastern United
States saw unionization radiating slowly but surely from
New York outward, although in 1966 not all New York's
hospitals, by far, were organized by unions.

Non-professionals played a vital role in the life of any
hospital, and no hospital could get along without their
services. So complex had the modern hospital become that
one, Yale-New Haven Hospital, listed 25 different services,
with subdivisions ranging from motor vehicle maintenance
to the dietary department. All these subdivisions had a
specific and immediate impact on the welfare of the patient.

There were laboratory assistants, pharmacists, surgical
technicians, orderlies, ward clerks, cooks, laundry workers, maintenance men, and dozens of other workers in the
hospital.

One doctor who complained about the level of service

in one of New York City's finest hospitals wondered why hospitals with their complex staffs could not give the same level of service that a good hotel gave.

One patient at the Los Angeles County Hospital discovered cockroaches climbing into her water glass.

Her charge was brought to the attention of Roger Egeberg, Medical Director of the Los Angeles Department of Charities, and he answered:

"We are accused of unsanitary conditions by permitting cockroaches to infest the hospital. The hospital handles large quantities of food daily and has hundreds of visitors. Where such a large quantity of food is handled there is always a danger of infestation. The hospital maintains a full time crew of exterminators and on the rare occasions where infestation is discovered they are called in and the condition corrected immediately. There is less infestation of this kind in the Los Angeles County Hospital than may be found at times in well-kept private homes . . ."

The director's response was an explanation, but it did not change the fact that carelessness on some employee's part kept the hospital from being as clean as a good hotel.

In its defense, let it be said that Los Angeles County Hospital probably had the most severe problems of any hospital in America, for it was large and cumbersome— the largest hospital in America—in a county that had grown so rapidly, every human problem was multiplied and exacerbated.

Hospital employees—some of whom the patient never even saw—had a direct effect on the actual physical well-being of the patient, the result depending on how well trained, efficient, and careful they were.

One day an orderly at a Vermont hospital left some colorless bichloride of mercury (a strong solution that is poisonous if taken internally) on a patient's bedside table. The patient drank some of the poison and died shortly thereafter. After the family of the patient sued the hospital, the court decided that the hospital (or one of its employees) *had* been careless, but the patient had died of natural causes. (He had cancer.)

In one hospital in upstate New York an aide mistakenly picked up the wrong bottle when mixing the babies' formula, and several babies fell seriously ill as a result.

Another incident involving babies occurred in October, 1964, at New York City's Cumberland Hospital. One day, while performing routine circumcisions, resident physicians at the hospital noticed that the blood of two babies was abnormally dark. They also saw that the babies' lips and fingernails were turning blue. They called the chief of pediatrics, who ordered a check on other babies in the nursery. In all, five babies were found to have these symptoms of what the doctors said was methemoglobinemia. They were turning into "blue babies." The babies were treated, and they responded quickly, but the problem remained. Tests showed that 21 others were affected, and the search for the reason began. The cause of the illness was finally discovered: a poisonous substance in the ink with which the name of the hospital was lettered on the diapers of these babies.

Every diaper was labeled in the laundry room before it was put into use in the hospital. Then it was supposed to be washed and sterilized. A laundry-room aide had been simply sterilizing diapers when there was a shortage, bypassing the necessary washing process.

The problem of securing adequate and qualified help in

all fields of hospital employment was difficult, at least for some hospitals (i.e., Rutland, Vermont, might not have a nursing shortage, but Winfield, Alabama, did).

In the spring of 1965, the United States Department of Labor moved to help solve the problem of manpower shortage in an agreement with the American Hospital Association which would bring government sponsorship to training programs for employees in 300 American hospitals. The New Jersey Hospital Association, which developed that state's emergency program, was chosen to lead the way for the AHA. These hospitals were to plan training for nurses' aides, surgical technicians, laboratory assistants, orderlies, ward clerks, and others. When they finished, there should be standards for training employees in hospitals. One of the problems of the past was that standards did not exist on a national basis.

Labor problems came to hospitals as "industrial" problems only in the years since the end of World War II, during which so many changes came to American society. But, as Editor Robert Cunningham of *The Modern Hospital* said: "it seems likely that hospital labor is going to be organized," and first in most big cities and industrial areas. The reason for this organization, as Dr. Henry Pratt, director of New York Hospital put it, was the exploitation of the workers in hospitals over a number of years.

Several states, including Minnesota and New York, outlawed strikes in hospitals. Nebraska seemed to have few hospital labor problems, partly because of its less turbulent political history. Alaska's hospitals were not union-conscious, but those in Hawaii were.

The extent of union activity seemed to be directly related to working conditions and wages in the hospital.

The modern struggle for unionization of hospital employees began in 1948 at Detroit's Harper Hospital, which refused to deal with any union at all. There was a strike and there have been other strikes since, in and around large cities. The most recent of these was the outcome, in a sense, of earlier strikes that occurred in New York City in 1959 and 1962. Hospital workers struck in both years for the right to join a union and have the union recognized by the hospitals. The New York City strikes came as a shock to the city and the state. The second was settled only when Governor Nelson Rockefeller intervened, and as a result of the settlement the New York legislature passed a law which forbade hospital strikes but gave hospital workers the right to join unions and bargain collectively with hospitals. Compulsory arbitration was to be the solution to hospital labor difficulties. The Rockefeller program applied only to New York City, not to New York State, and after a few months it became apparent that there was a move to extend unionization to hospitals outside the city limits.

Bronxville, an exclusive commuter community in Westchester County, was the point chosen for the attack of the Drug and Hospital Employees Union, Local 1199. The overall plan called for organization of 26 voluntary hospitals in Westchester County. Bronxville's was to be the first.

The organization program began when union officials attempted to meet with the administrator and the board of trustees of the Lawrence Hospital, to talk about organization. The Board of Trustees would not countenance such a meeting.

Negotiations, or overtures, continued. Then, in January,

1965, having worked among the 500 employees of the hospital for some time, the union called a strike.

Pickets went out in 22-degree weather to patrol the hospital. Near the end of January, 225 policemen and sheriff's deputies were called out to police 475 pickets.

The issues were union recognition, wages, and working conditions. Lawrence Hospital salaries had begun at $1.25 an hour, but when faced with union agitation the hospital had raised them, before the strike, to $1.50 an hour. The union men said that money was important, but less so than the right to join a union and be represented.

The strike became a social issue in Bronxville. Students from Sarah Lawrence College joined the pickets, largely on a civil-rights basis. (Most of the striking workers were Negroes.)

The Bronxville strike was complicated by civil-rights issues and charges that the Bronxville citizens were practicing Jim Crow. In fact, Bronxville always had been a closed community—Negroes were indeed not welcome there. Jews and Catholics were only tolerated in Bronxville, and were a very small minority.

When the strike began in January, a handful of people in the community supported the strikers and their right to organize.

Scores of matrons in the community came to the hospital to carry bedpans and give their services as menial laborers in the cause of keeping the hospital open. The strike did not cripple the hospital; the union claimed that some 140 of the 175 service employees went out on strike, and the hospital claimed that only about 60 were striking. The strike did cause some difficulty. One doctor mopped floors one day. He received not nearly so much acclaim

for this act of humanitarianism as criticism for publicly refusing to serve as medical advisor to the family of one of
the two Bronxville women who actively supported the
strike.

Usually the matrons and doctors and volunteer workers
who manned the mops and pails and bedpans during such
a walkout would gain some sympathy from at least a segment of the press, but it was hard to work up sympathy
for the closed community of Bronxville. Pickets were ar-
rested and there was some violence, apparently begun by
those in authority, and not by the strikers. Eventually the
right of collective bargaining was extended even to Bronxville, and the strike ended. The union had accepted a
pledge that it would be allowed to organize the workers
if it could.

In the complex society of the 1960's unionization was
bound to spread, as many responsible hospital administrators predicted.[3] It would spread more slowly after strikes
such as those in Bronxville, and those in New York two
and a half years earlier, because hospital administrators
tended to be more closely attuned to events in their field
than the industrialists of the 1920's and 1930's. Dissatisfaction in hospitals was concerned almost entirely with wages,
hours, and workers' benefits. Progressive hospitals were
moving to correct these problems in behalf of their employees.

What were the problems between hospitals and service
employees below the professional level? Here are some of
them:

One employee in the kitchen at Mt. Sinai Hospital in
New York City was sick for several days. It had been Mt.
Sinai's practice to ask workers who were out sick to call

in every day. This worker did not call in, and Mt. Sinai docked her pay. After the union came to Mt. Sinai such practices became matters for grievance discussions.

At the Flushing Hospital in Queens, New York City, maids in the housekeeping department argued with the management and among themselves about days off. Some wanted rotating days off, while others wanted fixed days off. The matter was settled by the grievance committee and management.

In another New York City Hospital, kitchen workers complained because they were charged for the dishes they broke. In still another the workers wanted vacation pay to be given to them before they went on their vacations, and not after they returned.

On the union's part, Local 1199 undertook to give its union members some additional training in union leadership. This resolved some problems for hospital management, too, because it stopped complaints that were not valid grievances, and ended some unnecessary bickering.

Any bickering or confusion in a hospital makes the patient's life difficult. Untrained and careless hospital workers can, for example, spread staphylococcus bacteria around the hospital very quickly. (Doctors say that staphylococcus infection—common in hospitals—is carried from person to person.)

Good hospitals see that their non-professional help is of the highest caliber, trying to solve the problem of giving service in hospitals that is "as good as that in hotels."

Chapter Ten

SPECIAL
SERVICES

In the hospital the patient may be at the mercy of doctors he does not know and never sees. This is unlikely to happen to a patient who is admitted by his own doctor, but it may to the charity patient who applies to a hospital and takes whatever medical care he is given.

In the hospital the welfare of the patient may also depend on services rendered by other persons that he either never sees or seldom sees. The hospital laboratory is one of these. Modern medicine is very much dependent on laboratory science, and good medicine and good hospitalization could not be practiced without fine laboratories. The laboratory technician in the middle 1960's was as important as the registered nurse to the proper care of patients in American hospitals.

The laboratory played a vital role in the case of the unwashed dye in the babies' diapers at Brooklyn's Cumberland Hospital. A few days after the hospital had shut down its nursery, and brought a score of toxicologists,

149

epidemiologists, hospital administration experts, and engineers to discover that there was unwashed dye in the babies' diapers, it was suddenly shut down again when pediatricians and laboratory workers mistakenly diagnosed several new cases of this strange "blue baby" illness.

Blood tests made in the hospital's laboratories seemed to show that 21 more children and nine hospital employees had traces of the same illness. The only problem was that the count, and the finding of a repetition of the disorder, were both the result of faulty work in the hospital's laboratory. The technician who was responsible for the tests made an error in computation, and hysteria was the result. The city health department repeated the tests in its own laboratories, and found no problems.

The New York Health Department then joined in the general hysteria and ordered a check made on the competence of the city's 400 laboratories. Health Commissioner George James promised to investigate all equipment in public and private laboratories, blood banks, and all other medical facilities in the city.

Eventually all came back to normal; it was, however, an illustration of what could happen if a hospital's laboratory suddenly became inoperative or began giving out the wrong answers.

Unfortunately there was no single standard for hospital and medical laboratories in the United States in 1965. New York State, for example, did not set up modern standards for laboratory procedures, or establish qualifications for laboratory directors, until the spring of 1964. At about that time, in New York City, five proprietary hospitals were ordered by the City Health Department either to correct what the department called "alarming" conditions in the laboratories or to close them. After July 1, 1965, laboratories would also be forced to submit periodic reports on their tests. The state standards were designed by the legislators more to protect upstate people than those of New York City, for controls of a sort had been exercised by the city before, while elsewhere in New York, as in other areas, nearly anyone could open a clinical laboratory. In New York, before 1965, clinical laboratories were opened and operated by former salesmen, medical corpsmen, and a tree surgeon.

Medical authorities have estimated that 15 percent of the ailments that come to the eyes of a doctor pose diagnostic questions that can only be answered, or are best answered, by laboratory tests, so the laboratory is a vital part of the health center or hospital. A bad laboratory is worse than useless. A study in New York City in 1965 showed that when Dr. Morris Schaeffer, director of the city's Department of Laboratories, gave "mystery specimens" to the laboratories of a number of small hospitals (150 beds or less) he found that nearly all of them failed his test. The technicians could not analyze the substances. He said these same technicians also often failed other tests; they were unable to make bacteria diagnosis, they made mistakes in blood typing and in simple chemical tests.

Medical technology is a far more skilled occupation than the average hospital patient ever considers. Ninety-five percent of America's hospitals operated their own chemical laboratories in 1964. In Waterbury, Connecticut, the Waterbury Hospital operated a school for technicians in collaboration with four colleges and universities, a program not unlike that of many other schools and hospitals. Students attended three years of college, studying medical technology; then they put in their fourth year at the hospital school under direction of a pathologist. After this they received a Bachelor of Science degree.

The pathologist, who supervises the laboratory of any reasonably-sized hospital, works in three fields. He is responsible for the examination of all tissues removed surgically, he oversees the clinical pathology or laboratory work, and he is concerned with pathological anatomy. Only the first two concerns are usually of interest in the hospital patient, but in these the pathologist's services are vital. Is he scientist or is he practicing physician? This question is a matter for struggle still within the medical and hospital professions, as discussed earlier. Whatever he is, the hospital cannot do without him, any more than it can do without the radiologist, the anesthesiologist, and the physiatrist, whose specialty is returning injured human tissues to their normal functions.

Outside medical talk, the study of physiatry would seem to be a hospital function and hardly any other. In many hospitals they call the department the Department of Physical Medicine. It is concerned with diagnosis, but also with recovery from illnesses. Twenty-one percent of American Hospitals maintain occupational-therapy departments; forty-eight percent maintain physical-therapy departments. These therapists work under the physical medicine department in a hospital. It is at once an age-old and very new specialty, the newness of it being geared to the realization by modern medicine that persons who would once have been on the human discard pile can be brought back to near-normal and very useful lives in society. Like a pathologist, a physiatrist must study medicine, must intern, and then must begin his special studies.

In 1965 not all hospitals had full-time doctors in any of the specialties. Some general practitioners still maintained that either they or a nurse-anesthetist were quite capable of giving anesthesia. They regarded anesthesiology as a highly overrated specialty.

Only in recent years had doctors in America generally accepted anesthesiology as the "exacting science" that the specialists have said it is. Dr. Joseph Artusio, Jr., chief anesthesiologist at the New York Hospital, and Professor of Anesthesiology and *Surgery* at Cornell University Medical College, said this, writing in The New York Hospital *News* in the spring of 1965:

"There is no such thing as simple anesthesia. All anesthetics are potent drugs. To administer the correct drugs in the correct amounts, to watch over each detail of the unconscious patient's condition and to return him to the conscious state without any harm, these are the responsibilities of the anesthesiologist."

In terms of time it takes to become such a specialist, obviously the specialty should be a full partner of surgery. Six years of study were required *after medical school.*

And what have the specialists done for medicine and hospital procedures? This particular doctor has developed methoxyfluorane, a nonflammable, nonexplosive anesthetic.

Anesthesiologists say that the methods of making a patient unconscious for surgery must be varied in different cases. If a patient has a lung, liver, or cardiac condition, he must be treated quite differently from a patient who has no such complications.

All this led to a serious question in American hospital practices of the 1960's. Was it good enough to have general practitioners or nurse-anesthetists in charge of anesthesia for patients undergoing surgery?

A case occurred in the summer of 1965 in which a young

woman died after an oxygen machine exploded in the hospital delivery room. This case involved a general practitioner at the Connecticut hospital mentioned in an earlier chapter, and a suit for more than a million dollars was brought by the family of the dead woman against hospital, doctor, and manufacturers. This particular incident was all the more notable because the hospital had suffered a serious setback from what was in effect a doctors' strike, a few years earlier, over just such matters as the question of anesthesia and other medical specialties.

Anesthesiologists said that it was not safe to have anesthetics in the hands of persons other than those with vast experience and intensive training in this science. Anesthesia mistakes accounted for a number of hospital deaths in the 1960's, but the fact that there were so few anesthesiologists in America even by 1965 was one reason the matter may have been given less than prominent public discussion by the medical and hospital leaders. There was no use telling the public that an anesthesiologist was necessary at every operation when it might not be possible for a small hospital to persuade an anesthesiologist to locate in the community. In areas where old-fashioned medicine was practiced, some general practitioners still said the anesthesiologist was unnecessary. In the teaching hospitals there was no question about the value of this specialty, any more than there was about the importance of pathology.

The pathologist is one of the most important men in the hospital, particularly to the patient undergoing surgery. In a hospital which is certified by the Joint Commission, every piece of tissue taken from a human body must be examined by a pathologist to see if it is diseased or healthy, and to diagnose any disease that affects it.

Here the potential patient thinks of cancer, but there is another reason as important: the protection of patients at large against unscrupulous practitioners who might operate simply for money, without regard to the need to the patient. There was more of this in 1965 than anyone outside the medical and hospital professions could possibly know.

The third important doctor in the hospital that the patient may never see or consider is the radiologist. His work sometimes meant the difference between life and death as when, one day in New York City, a 65-year-old man was brought into a hospital after an automobile accident. He was treated in the emergency room and allowed to go home. He was kept at the hospital for five hours, and then was discharged. His condition was reported as satisfactory.

Several hours later a radiologist was running through the routine X-rays taken the day before at this New York City hospital when he saw something that indicated that the man ought to be brought back to the hospital immediately. Others had studied the X-rays and had believed them to be normal. The radiologist saw an irregular line near the left hipbone.

The next day a telegram was sent to this man's home in Brooklyn urging him to return to the hospital's emergency room to see a physician. It came too late. The accident victim had died hours earlier, and when his body was brought for autopsy the postmortem examination showed death was caused by a fractured pelvis with massive internal hemorrhage and shock.

Radiology is important for diagnostic work and for treatment, of course, and X-ray technicians with perhaps two years of training are often in charge of small hospital

X-ray departments. But how well trained were these technicians to read X-rays and interpret them in 1965, or how well trained were general practitioners to do the same? It would appear that the services of a radiologist were very important in any American health center in the 1960's.

In a hospital where a radiologist was in charge of his specialty, in the 1960's there was far more than an X-ray machine to be considered. At Waterbury Hospital Dr. Joseph M. James, chief radiologist, had in 1965 a Magnascanner, which could locate blood clots in the human body, radioactive isotopes, fluoroscopic devices, including a new $49,000 "image intensifier" which brought television into the X-ray room, and many other instruments and devices.

The X-ray department of a hospital may make some 70 or 80 diagnostic X-rays a day, and these can usually be performed by a technician with two years of training. But if the hospital were to go in for treatment; for the G. I. (gastrointestinal) series where the patient swallows barium and it is studied as it goes through the digestive tract; air studies of the brain, radio-opaque dye studies of the lungs, spine, arteries, and organs; and for the radium or X-ray treatment of malignancy—these were all matters for the supervision of an expert.

Another important department of the American hospital, which the patient might never see, was the pharmacy or drug room. If the hospital had 100 beds or more it usually had a pharmacy, which was controlled by a registered licensed pharmacist, a college graduate who specialized in studying the uses and compounding of drugs. In the matter of drugs and drug rooms, hospitals were more careful than perhaps in any other non-medical department, and consequently few cases of misapplication of drugs were reported, and fewer suits were filed by far than in other hazard departments. In Connecticut, Waterbury Hospital, with more than 300 beds, had three full-time pharmacists and one part-time pharmacist. Stafford Springs' Johnson Memorial Hospital had one part-time pharmacist, and so did Sharon Hospital, where the pharmacist also operated the village drug store.

Some smaller hospitals did not have staff pharmacists, but used the services of an outside pharmacist on a consulting basis, with the control of drugs placed in the hands of the chief nurse. That system was used at New Milford (Connecticut) Hospital, for one.

A system that was used in many small hospitals, and spread far beyond them, was a dispensing system for commonly-used drugs, called the Brewer system. It consisted of machine units which looked something like cigarette machines. Inside were packages and racks of drugs, perhaps 99 or 100 different drugs, packed in normal dosage or cycle units. When a nurse wanted a drug from the machine she put in a plate with her name on it, a plate with the name of the drug on it, and one with the patient's name, and out came the proper drug. The system is very nearly foolproof.

Hospitals had many different philosophies about the operation of their pharmacy departments. It was an area in which considerable profits could be made if the hospital chose to make of the pharmacy a profit-making department. This could be done from the noblest of motives, taking the position that the patient will pay what he would pay to an outside or independent pharmacy for drugs, then using the pharmacy profits to offset other losses in the general fund. It could also be done from base motives, particularly in proprietary hospitals.

Some hospitals made a flat charge of two or three dollars a week per patient for ordinary drugs, such as aspirin, mild sleeping tablets, and charcoal. One such, in 1963, spent $15,000 on its pharmacy and took in more than $22,000. It obviously made a profit on sale of drugs.

Others, such as Sharon Hospital, offered drugs at only slightly above the cost of purchase, and at a figure considerably lower than the patient would pay outside the hospital. In a non-profit hospital the only valid question for the patient was whether or not he, as a paying patient, was being asked to subsidize the drugs for charity patients. And even in that question, the fact was that in the hospital financing of the 1960's he was subsidizing many outside costs in his hospital bill.

Doctors had one serious complaint in relation to drug therapy in hospitals and where government authorities were paying for the patient's medical and hospital treatment. A dozen states restricted the drugs that might be prescribed for charity or welfare patients. In Pennsylvania, for example, a doctor must have the approval of a state welfare official before he could write a prescription which cost more than $10. In Utah, a doctor could not prescribe more than $15 worth of drugs for a welfare patient in a month—at least, the state would not pay for more.

In some states the state limited the number of refills of prescriptions. Nevada permitted none. Illinois permitted some, but they must be specified in advance.

It can be recognized by laymen that some of the terms used in this chapter, as well as some of the concepts, have arisen in the past twenty years. (Radioactive isotopes, for example.) One need not be a doctor or scientist to understand how vast have been the changes in modern medicine. The laboratory's function and its standards of training have changed as much. In fact, there was seldom just one laboratory in any good-sized hospital in 1965, but several departments which undertook the old laboratory functions. This was also true of X-ray rooms and other special departments. At Hartford Hospital, to cite one case, when the emergency rooms were being expanded, it occurred to the administration of the hospital that the logical place for the X-ray department was right there, and so the department was moved into that wing, where time has proved the decision to be proper.

Among the special hospital services which would increase in the 1960's and after—particularly with Medicare —were diagnostic services like tests in the laboratories, X-rays, electrocardiograms, and therapy that would be carried out in special departments. The physiatry or physical medicine department would be called on for more braces and artificial limbs, and for more treatment of arthritis and other crippling conditions.

Another special service offered by most hospitals was the emergency room, which had become a place both for treatment that was not truly "emergency" and for genuine emergency cases. Such cases in the latter category often came by ambulance, and the ambulance might be provided by a private concern, by the police or fire department, or by the hospital itself. There was no standardization of ambulance service in America in 1966. A traveller from one part of the United States might have no idea of how to get an ambulance in another part. In the cities of the Far West ambulance services were usually provided by private business firms, but the police had ambulances, and sometimes the fire departments too. In southern New England and parts of the other East Coast states, ambulance services were provided in small towns by volunteer fire departments. They were usually free services. Sharon, Connecticut, was typical. The ambulance in this town of 3,000 people was kept in the firehouse, across the street from the local bank and about two blocks from the hospital. In 1965 there was no full-time attendant in the firehouse, but when an ambulance was required a doctor or a layman telephoned the hospital switchboard, and the hospital telephone operator began scanning a list of volunteer firemen, calling them until she found one who could make the run. The fireman then rushed to the firehouse and took out the ambulance. One volunteer who was often called on was the groceryman in Cunningham's store, half a block from the firehouse. Another was the postmaster, working at the post office half a dozen blocks away. Sharon's system was effective and simple; the town had a new ambulance which cost some $17,000, and much of that money was given by grateful citizens who either had need to use the free service or who knew that it existed for their use.

In northern New England the system was quite different. There, perhaps as a hangover from the original days of colonization, the ambulance services were in the hands of funeral directors, who were almost always furniture dealers. In some places the same machine was used to transport the sick and the dead.

Among combination ambulance-emergency services, the Emergency Aid Program of Los Angeles County General Hospital was particularly advanced. It worked on the basis of providing the service first and worrying about the payment later, which was not always true in the United States, and was not always true with private California hospitals, many of which demanded deposits. (One of these private hospitals once threatened to refuse to *discharge* a patient until the bill was paid in full.)

In 1947 the Board of Supervisors of Los Angeles County contracted with 37 hospitals and 10 emergency clinics to treat emergency cases. This seemed a large number, but Los Angeles County covers four thousand square miles. In spite of this number of treatment centers, some points in 1965 were still 40 miles from the nearest hospital.

On the same basis, the county contracted for emergency ambulance services with 47 ambulance companies. When an accident occurred, ambulances were rushed to the scene without concern for who was going to pay, and the injured were taken to the nearest medical aid facility, hospital, or clinic. The ambulance company then tried to collect from the people involved. If it was unable to do so, the county paid the bill. Ambulance charges were fixed ($15 for the call and $1 a mile for the second mile and thereafter).

Most cities have ambulance services, but not the city of New York. There, were it not for the city hospitals and a number of the voluntary hospitals, the people of the nation's largest city would have had no ambulance service at all in 1966. The hospitals bore the burden, along with the police department.

Every day from 88 to 110 ambulances were stationed at 15 municipal hospitals and 24 voluntary hospitals in the city. Each was manned by a driver and by an attendant who need not be trained in any of the healing arts. Until 1966 there was not even a requirement that driver and attendant be instructed in elementary Red Cross first aid

measures; and this minimum requirement was to be enforced only at municipal hospitals.

New York's ambulance service has been called the worst
in the United States. That charge was made by Dr. Robert
H. Kennedy, director of the Field Service of the American
College of Surgeons Committee on Trauma. Between 1960
and 1965, Dr. Kennedy studied the New York system on a
grant from the John A. Hartford foundation, and when he
was finished he rated New York at the bottom of American
cities, surpassed even by the undertakers who carry emergency cases as a sideline.

Police and some doctors told stories of people who were
seriously injured on the streets of the city and waited for
as long as an hour for an ambulance. Louisville police,
who handled ambulance calls themselves, said that they
answered them in five minutes. Los Angeles claimed a six
minute time lapse. In Moscow, the Russians claimed
twelve minutes. New York City's director of ambulance
services claimed in 1965 that calls were answered in 20 to
25 minutes. Although Dr. Kennedy said that speed was
a critical factor in less than eight percent of ambulance
cases, he gave New York a very low rating. He cited New
Jersey's emergency ambulance service, operated by volunteer rescue squads, as providing the best-trained and most
effective ambulance service in America.

Dr. Kennedy also recommended the Louisville system,
operated by the police, as one of the best. That city did
not use ambulances, but patrol cars which were nearly all
station wagons. The officers radioed ahead to a hospital,
delivered the patient, and within fifteen minutes he might
be on the operating table.

Fifteen years before 1965 the Hospital Council of
Greater New York studied the city's ambulance service

and made a number of major recommendations. The most important of these was that the police department should handle ambulance service. Others included a recommendation to increase the number of ambulance stations. But the New York City police department was reluctant to take on new responsibility; consequently, two-way radios were installed in the ambulances, the report was put aside, and no major change was made. In 1965, ambulance service was being handled by the 39 hospitals as noted earlier.

A study made by a New York newspaper showed why New York residents were tending in the 1960's to turn to the city's public and non-profit hospitals and ambulance services rather than to private doctors for assistance in times of emergency.

One night, a New Yorker suffered a heart attack. His wife called the family doctor and was told by the person who answered the telephone that the doctor would be there shortly. An hour went by, and no doctor appeared. The wife of the sick man called the telephone operator, who telephoned the police station and a voluntary hospital. Ambulance attendants and a policeman arrived, administered oxygen to the sick man, but did not want to move him until the family doctor came. Two hours after the first call to the doctor, in spite of repeated calls, he had not arrived. The man died.

The newspaper asked the family doctor why he had not responded to the call.

"Where I was and what I was doing is none of the family's business," said the doctor. "I was not available."

"I cannot always be at the phone waiting for patients to call. It is impossible for the doctor to be at the bedside of a patient every time he is needed."

Had the family *not* called the doctor, but simply the hospital, the man might have lived.

Whether or not Americans accept that doctor's attitude, it was very common among the members of the medical profession in the 1960's. One doctor on the staff of New York Hospital said that he was ashamed of his profession because this attitude was so prevalent. This particular doctor, who lived in mid-town Manhattan, responded to *all* pleas for house calls except in cases where it was believed a bone had been broken; then the doctor advised the patient to go directly to the hospital emergency room —but the doctor *met* the patient there. Such an attitude was so uncommon in the big cities in the 1960's that the voluntary and city hospitals were becoming the treatment centers, replacing doctors' offices.

In the two largest industrial areas of Connecticut, New Haven and Hartford, hospitals treated thousands more cases in the emergency rooms each year in the 1960's than they had a decade earlier. At Yale-New Haven Hospital some 50,000 patients were treated each year in the emergency facilities. A large percentage of the people of New Haven had come to look upon the Yale-New Haven Hospital as "their" medical center.

Another indication of the change in the role of the hospital emergency facilities was the situation at Hartford Hospital. In 1940 that hospital maintained four treatment rooms called emergency rooms. Some 1,500 patients a year visited those rooms. Most had suffered a serious accident or sudden illness in a public place. A quarter of a century later, the hospital was treating more than twice as many patients per month as it had in all 1940, and the emergency room had been expanded to include 17 rooms; it was a major part of the hospital, and at night was used as an emergency admitting ward for the hospital. Such change was happening in nearly every community hospital in America. "The public has come to think of the hospital as part of its community life," said one Hartford Hospital official. "This is good. However, it has its negative factors in that it does lead to a misconception of the department as something more than an *emergency* room."

So, in 1965, the public was using hospitals as health clinics, whether through emergency rooms or general clinics, and hospitalization did not always mean actual admission to the hospital, but simply the use of its facilities.

This kind of service has long been called "outpatient service" and with the high cost of hospitalization and the advances in modern medicine, it had grown in 1965 to the point where many who might have had to be hospitalized in past years could be treated and walk away from the hospital.

Most large hospitals operated clinics. Sometimes, as at hospitals like Mary Hitchcock Memorial in Hanover, New Hampshire, one might say that clinics operated hospitals. Under Mary Hitchcock's "closed staff" policy, patients were treated only by clinic doctors. Each patient then had the services of the clinic's specialists in every field of medicine. In an emergency it could be a bit difficult for the patient whose doctor was not a member of the clinic, because this was the region's only hospital other than a Veterans Administration Hospital.

At the best hospitals, clinic care had become an important specialty. Peter Bent Brigham Hospital in Boston once treated outpatients through specialty clinics; in 1965 these had been broken down into small general clinics. The reason: this way the patient was immediately assigned to a single doctor who became, in effect, his "family doctor." He examined the patient, recommended specialty care, and followed his progress. Thus a great hospital, which might be impersonal, was performing a personal function that had been largely abandoned in city areas by private doctors.

Hospital treatment of outpatients assumed enormous proportions in some areas. In Los Angeles more than 2,000 patients attended the Los Angeles County General Hospital's 65 clinics *every day*. That hospital in 1965 completed a new building at a cost of $7,000,000. All these facilities, including 3,151 beds, existed for the "medically indigent" of Los Angeles County, and for them alone.[1]

In Los Angeles County any person who can pay for hospital care goes either to a non-profit hospital or to a proprietary hospital. Emergency cases and patients too poor to pay are treated in Los Angeles County General. The hospital is actually operated by the county Department of Charities. The medically indigent receive good care, considering the problems of treating so many and the use of the huge facility involved.

It is not quite accurate to say that Los Angeles County General treats *only* the indigent, it also cares for all persons with communicable diseases and all who require psychiatric care. One of the unusually liberal aspects of California law holds that the government must care for the mentally ill, as a responsibility, whether or not the family can afford private facilities.

So in California, and southern California in particular, there is a high regard for public health, and there are few cases of persons needing medical attention who are unable to gain admission to hospitals.

After arrival at the hospital, the patient is treated or admitted without question. Later the matter of payment is brought up, and if the patient can pay he must. If he cannot, the county assumes the bill. But even the county does not accept the poor as "free" patients, if they have resources or property. Bills are rendered at the hospital's cost per day. (In 1965 the cost per day in the surgical section, for example, was $43 per day.) Even if the bills are not collectible, liens may be placed against property of the patients, or if the county suspects that they have resources, they may be taken to collection and to court. But no one is refused emergency hospital care in the county of Los Angeles, and the quality of this care is very high at the county hospital.

One of the most serious problems of emergency hospitalization at Los Angeles County General Hospital is caused by some of the 76 cities in the sprawling county. Most of these cities belonged to the county emergency-aid system, but not all were willing to cooperate. Consequently, in August, 1964, a seventeen-month-old-child lay dying from drowning in a home in Anaheim's residential area, and a fire department rescue squad which was two minutes away refused to go to the child's aid because the family home was thirty feet outside the Anaheim city limits. Otherwise the rescue squad would have rushed to the scene, treated the child, and dashed with it to a hospital.

California has an automatic emergency system. Many other regions do not, but California's advanced plan for emergency hospital treatment was spreading to other areas of the country. In the spring of 1965 New Jersey went even further: the first *statewide* emergency network of hospitals was established there. New Jersey was divided into six hospital regions, which serve the state's twenty-one counties. The New Jersey Hospital Association established this program, linking 24 major hospitals by two-way radio. They could cover any emergency in any section of the state within minutes. In 1961, the city of Dallas inaugurated emergency service. Hospitals and ambulances acted first and worried later, taking any injured or ill person to the hospital of his choice, if he was able to make a choice. If not, the ambulance drivers were instructed to take patients to the nearest hospital, or to follow the instructions of the police.

Perhaps the most dramatic of special services of the hospital in the 1960's was the operating room. In the 1960's, complicated and expensive operations like open-heart surgery demanded the services of a team of specially trained people, and hundreds of thousands of dollars worth of equipment.[2] An open-heart operation used the expensive heart-lung machine, which takes over the pumping and oxygenation of the blood so that the heart may be stopped and repaired. So complicated an operation could not be performed by one man. It demanded a surgeon; an assistant surgeon; a cardiologist, whose concern is with the heart itself and who treats any condition that is related to heart disease; an assistant cardiologist, who monitors the equipment which shows pulse beat, respiration, and other signs of life; a scrub nurse, who serves the surgeon; a technician, who watches the machines to keep them working properly; a circulating nurse, who brings all supplies to the scrub nurse; an anesthesiologist, who decides on and administers anesthesia; an orderly, who assists the nurses; a pump operator, who manages the heart-lung machine; an operator's assistant, who assists the pump operator and operates the auxiliary pump in case the main pump fails.

Still, with all the facilities available in medical centers for various kinds of surgery, America's surgical facilities in 1965 were totally inadequate to meet major disaster. This information was first brought to public attention by Dr. Solomon Garb, of the University of Missouri School of Medicine, in 1964 in a book called *Disaster Handbook*.

Doctor Garb wrote in terms of the 200-bed hospital that existed in so many medium-sized American cities. It was a good-sized hospital and might employ four or five hundred people. But in a disaster this hospital could handle perhaps only 20 seriously injured patients per day, when the need might be for ten times that many. A 350-bed hospital, with a ten-room operating suite, should be able to handle 70 disaster patients a day, and could do so by pressing non-surgical helpers into action. But there was one generally unknown factor in America's surgical unpreparedness for disaster: the shortage of extra supplies of surgical instruments.

In order to be used on a continuing basis, an operating room must have a complete duplicate set of instruments, since after an operation instruments must be cleaned, packed, and sterilized. Nearly *no* American hospitals had such duplicate sets in 1965.

Dr. Garb studied the events that occurred in Worcester, Massachusetts, a few years earlier when a tornado ripped through that city, injuring scores of people. The wounded were brought to hospitals, and the surgeons worked around the clock to save them. But they had too few instruments, and in order to keep on operating, the instruments were passed from room to room as needed, merely washed under the water tap as best they could be. The result was that 98 percent of the patients developed infections after the operations.

In spite of such shortages in the operating room, however, it was there that doctors made the use of the finest, most specialized equipment.

In the 1960's the advances in medical and surgical techniques that could be practiced in hospitals would be called miracles by practitioners of a half century before. The matter of "Death" had once been considered final, but no more. People were dying and being revived, arms were being severed and sewed back on, recovering normal functions, whole organs were being exchanged, and it was apparent that it would become medically possible soon to give people new hearts and new blood vessels. The treatment had become almost unbelievable.

Take the case of Bobby Munz, a New York boy who suffered a scratch on the leg one day while playing basketball. He went to the doctor when it became infected, and the doctor gave him antibiotics. The treatment had no noticeable effect. He went to a hospital and was given thirty million units of penicillin three times a day. The infection persisted.

A medical consultant was called in and he recommended transfer to Mt. Sinai Hospital, one of New York City's most advanced teaching institutions. Bobby Munz was brought there with an atypical pneumonia, his lungs filled, and bloody fluid coming from his nose and mouth.

While he was being examined his condition grew worse by the moment, and he twice fell into what the doctors called a condition of "anoxic death"—death from lack of oxygen.

When the boy turned black in the face, there was something to be done, for Mt. Sinai Hospital had a new medical weapon called a "hyperbaric oxygen chamber," in which a patient could be placed, sealed, and surrounded with pure oxygen under such pressure that it seeped into the tissues from outside, rather than coming in from the lungs alone. This relieved the lungs of their burden, and brought oxygen to tissues that would otherwise "die."

Bobby Munz was put into the chamber, after the resident surgeon assigned to the chamber had performed a tracheotomy and made it possible for him to breathe again. He was kept in the chamber under two atmospheres of pressure, and then under 1.5 atmospheres, of pressure, for twenty-four hours. From time to time the doctors tried to cut down the pressure, fearing the effects of so much oxygen for so long a time, but each time they tried to cut down, the boy began to fail and they had to restore the pressure.

At the end of that day, he was removed and put in the hospital's intensive care unit, but within a few hours he was back in the chamber again, almost as badly off as before. He remained there another 16 hours, and then the crisis really was over.

This technique was also used to save a 32-year-old mother who was suffering from gas gangrene after having delivered a child. She would almost certainly have died had not the chamber been available. A few days later a similar unit was used to save the life of a Boston boy at Boston Children's Hospital Medical Center, who was also suffering from gangrene after suffering a compound fracture of the arm.

The doctor who treated this boy in Boston noted that the hyperbaric oxygen treatment had been the thin difference between life and death in all the patients treated.

So the questions were raised: how many people could have these treatments? What use was to be made of the remarkable advances of medical and surgical techniques that were flooding the world in the 1960's?

The hyperbaric oxygenation chamber cost $750,000. It required the services of surgeons and an eight-member crew of technicians and nurses. It was hard to see how any but one of the teaching hospitals and medical centers could afford or utilize such a piece of equipment.

The changing functions of the hospital were nowhere better illustrated than in the law which established the "regional medical complexes." This idea was based on the need to eliminate competition between hospitals for such important equipment as the heart-lung machines and oxygenation chambers, and to make these facilities and others available to the widest range of the population.

The American Hospital Association backed this law, to establish 32 medical complexes around the country, linking medical schools, hospitals, and research centers in an attack on the three great killers of adults: heart disease, cancer, and stroke. The AHA's backing was based on its concern over the gap between medicine and hospitalization as it ought to be practiced and as it was practiced. It wanted to go further, to bring the 600 approved teaching hospitals which were not affiliated with medical schools into the research program. This was not done. Maybe it would be done at some future date.

Other groups opposed the program, for various reasons. The AMA's basic opposition was based on its usual formula: this was government medicine. But a group of medical researchers at Harvard opposed the measure for quite a different reason. They said that the multi-million dollar program was designed to attack diseases that were the major killers after the age of 65. What they wanted was an attack on the diseases that killed infants and young adults.

In the society of the 1960's there was a subtle change

from the past, a worry by some that with all the emphasis on the preservation of life to some point past three score and ten, the young were being bypassed for the aging. The marvels of twentieth century surgery, the organ transplants and the discoveries that could save so many lives once lost, gave confidence to many and worry to some. The Harvard group said "One must not lose sight of the fact that medical care is for all the living as well as for the moribund."

However, it was true that there is reason for massive assault on the great killer diseases. Lung cancer, for example, caused about 15 deaths per 100,000 people in 1963 in the United States.[3] Various forms of heart disease killed off some 600,000 Americans each year, according to World Health Organization statistics, or about twice as many as cancer killed. Other countries were worried by malaria and tuberculosis. Those killers had long been defeated in the United States, but new problems arose to plague health authorities—such as a 45 percent increase in venereal disease in 1961.[4]

Special services would increase in the decade ahead, most health authorities agreed. One of the major efforts was to be the attack on mental illness. American public health authorities reported to the WHO their concern about the slow turnover of patients and the slow progress of treatment which sharply reduced the effectiveness of the hospitals concerned with mental illness and the treatment of retardation. The hospital's role in seeking answers to such difficult questions was bound to be increased.

Chapter Eleven

THE PATIENT IN
THE HOSPITAL—I

Getting into a hospital could be as simple as picking up the telephone and calling the family doctor—or it could become so complicated that the patient died before he could be admitted.

For the potential patient there were three ways in 1965 to get into the average community or general service hospital. One, and the most usual, was by way of the front door and the admissions office. The second was by way of the side door and the ambulance service. The third was by way of the emergency room.

At the 100 bed Sharon Hospital in Connecticut, for example, any person could appear, demand entrance, and be received if hospitalization was indicated. This was not true at all hospitals, or even at all community hospitals. For those who had it, a Blue Cross card could be an open sesame. The card represented hospitalization insurance, and a guarantee to the hospital that most of its bill, at least, would be paid. Those who declared themselves to be charity patients usually had no difficulty in gaining admission to hospitals, if they came through the proper channels. The state, county, or city paid all or a portion of their bills if they were welfare recipients. But there was a problem for a wide range of persons: the "medically indigent." These people were not on public dole; they supported themselves and fed and clothed their families; yet when illness struck they were not in a position to pay or guarantee their hospital bills.

There were cases of this kind at Sharon Hospital as well as every other community hospital in the country. Here is one:

In the summer of 1965 a woman from nearby New York came to Sharon Hospital and demanded admission. She was about to give birth to a child—her ninth. All of her children had been born in Sharon Hospital. The usual practice at Sharon Hospital was for a doctor to seek admission for a patient, and nurses did not admit patients without the official sanction of a doctor. Sharon being a 100 bed hospital, without residents or interns, it was necessary for the secretary in the admissions office to seek the advice of the senior nurse in charge of the nursing station. An obstetrician of the hospital staff was telephoned, spoke to the patient, and ordered her admitted. This patient had an outstanding bill of nearly $600 from previous admissions for childbirth, but the outstanding bill made no difference. She was admitted and put to bed. The only difference between her admission and any other was that the admissions clerk made sure that the woman was put to bed in a ward and not in a semi-private room.

The woman was delivered of her baby without incident, and in a few days mother and child were ready to leave the hospital. In the business office, the assistant to the controller wanted to know how the woman intended to pay this bill. She was vague about it but promised to pay.

Several months went by and the bill was still uncollected; but when that same woman would apply again for hospitalization she would have it at that same hospital, even though there was very little chance that the total bill could ever be collected.

Most unpleasant stories involving admission to hospitals concerned emergency cases, because these were the cases where speed was essential. In September, 1961, in Tucson, a four-year-old boy was struck by a car in front of his own house. He was rushed to a hospital, a public institution, but he was not admitted. "We are awfully overcrowded," said the admitting nurse, who suggested then that the boy be taken to a private physician or perhaps to a private hospital, for this was a case involving a family which could afford to pay. The boy was taken to a private hospital, and there he was found to be suffering from internal injuries which were not apparent to the nurse at the county hospital. (The newspapers soon had the story and not long afterward doctors in the community asked that the emergency room at the public hospital be closed down entirely.)

The admitting problem in 1965 was a difficult one in emergencies. Just how much of an emergency is involved? —that is a question some doctor, nurse, or admissions clerk must answer in each case. One day in 1963, for example, at a general hospital in El Paso, Texas, a soldier appeared who had been injured in a traffic accident. Doctors at that hospital refused to treat the soldier. They told him that he was to go to a military hospital instead. The General Hospital's policy was to treat military personnel only in "dire emergency." And yet, in a reversal of this high-handedness, the Veterans Administration Hospital at White River Junction, Vermont, made it known in its community that it would treat any patients in emergency, although only military veterans were supposed to be eligible for entrance into the VA hospital system.

No matter by what method the patient entered the hospital, once he was in, treatment and professional and service care were the same, regardless of wealth, race, or religion. Or almost the same. Charity cases were generally placed in wards, where according to one hospital administrator they received the best care of any in the hospital, since there was constant nursing supervision there. The wealthy generally chose seclusion in private rooms. The matter of race, in relation to professional care, was of less importance than it was a decade before. Yet discrimination against Negro patients still existed in the 1960's. In the South the discrimination ran in several patterns.[1] The proprietory hospital pattern was part of it. Some southern hospitals did not receive Negro patients. One in North Carolina said there were no Negroes resident in the area, which might be like Bronxville, New York, saying there were no Negroes in that area—the discriminatory exclusiveness of Bronxville kept Negroes out.

In some southern hospitals Negro patients were relegated to the oldest wings, perhaps even to rooms and wards that were never meant for patient care. In nearly all southern hospitals Negroes were housed separately from whites.

A large hospital in Norfolk, Virginia, reported that it indulged in no discriminatory practices whatsoever. The Herrmann Hospital in Houston said that "colored" patients had been admitted since the opening of the hospital in 1925 and that no discrimination had ever been prac-

ticed. Two Kentucky hospitals said that there was discrimination among patients only on one level: colored adults
and white adults were not housed in the same rooms, and
one hospital administrator from Frankfort noted that he
had found more discrimination in hospitals in the North
than in his own.

From Gulfport, Mississippi, one hospital had this to report:

"We have agreed to comply with the Civil Rights Act
of 1964. Are deliberately attempting to eliminate all areas
of discrimination."

From Helena, Arkansas, came another frank comment:

"These problems will be solved in time. Progress is being made. The area is 50 percent white and 50 percent
Negro."

From the West and the Far West came the most positive answers. An administrator in Idaho asked "Why
should we discriminate?" Another in Spokane said neither
race nor religion posed any problem at all. From Anchorage an administrator wrote: "The Negro, the White, the
Japanese, the Chinese, the Hawaiians, the Filipinos, the
Eskimos, the Aleuts . . . all are placed together and we
find the people in this area most unconcerned about these
differences." From Hilo came the brief note that discrimination of any kind was not a problem anywhere in Hawaii.

Discrimination because of race was very apparent in
hospitals in Tuscaloosa, Alabama. Tuscaloosa was the
headquarters of one of the Ku Klux Klans in America, the
one operated by Imperial Wizard Robert Shelton.

In the early spring of 1959 it came to the attention of
the Ku Klux Klan that some integrated practices were be-

ing carried out at Hale Memorial tuberculosis hospital, operated for the State of Alabama under the direction of Dr. Horace White, who had come to Tuscaloosa from Oregon.

This western administrator had ordered white orderlies and practical nurses to give enemas and other treatments that involved touching Negro patients.

Several of the practical nurses and orderlies complained. The Klan went into action. An "uppity" Negro orderly was taken out of the hospital grounds one night, driven into the countryside, and given a beating and the fright of his life.

A few days later, Dr. White discharged three white employees for refusing to care for Negro patients. None of these was a registered nurse. "The only thing white nurses do for Negro patients is measure out medicine because no colored nurses are available," said one employee.

Soon Dr. White was under harassment from the Ku Klux Klan. His life was threatened. He was given 48 hours to get out of town, and the lives of his wife and family were threatened. Without backing from the board of trustees or anyone else in Tuscaloosa, Dr. White resigned his post and he and his family left the hospital. So did the nursing director and several other professional employees. The Ku Klux Klan won its victory. It also came very close to destroying the hospital.

"White did not know the southern customs and not being told, he did some things that did not fit the book," said Dr. Otis L. Jordan, the chairman of the board of trustees of Hale Memorial Hospital.

Where racial discrimination did not exist in hospitals, patients received the same type of care—good or bad, depending on the standards and facilities of the hospital. Neglect and impersonality were problems, but they were general problems.

The feeling of patients that no one cared often occurred in larger hospitals. In one case, a registered nurse took her teen-age daughter to a Hollywood hospital one day in the summer of 1963. The girl was to have a relatively serious eye operation the next day. The room had been reserved, and mother and daughter went there. The mother helped her daughter get into bed. She rang the buzzer to let the floor nurse know that they were there—for no one had escorted them to the room and no one had seen them come along the corridor. This registered nurse waited, with her nervous daughter, for an hour before any hospital personnel arrived at the room. Then, she said, she was very upset about going away to leave her daughter overnight, because the atmosphere seemed so cold and callous.

In large public hospitals there is sometimes danger that the impersonality will result in mix-ups and inhumanities. In one New York hospital, two patients were able to assume each other's identities without the authorities ever discovering. The change was brought to light a year and a half later when the hospital administrator notified relatives that one of the patients was critically ill. Relatives, who had stayed away all that time, came to see her, and discovered that the patient who bore their relative's name was not their relative at all but quite another person. Their relative had died and been buried under another name nearly two years before.

Patients sometimes wondered why it was that they entered a hospital, were put into bed, and then began living a role in a drama which went on about them, and which they were never allowed to understand.

One patient in a private room in a New York hospital telephoned the hospital in order to find out how he was, and did find out. The nurse at the nursing station gave him a very encouraging report on the telephone, although she had flatly refused to tell him anything in person, including his temperature. A patient in another hospital tried this ploy, but was detected by an alert telephone operator and given no information at all.

Why should not a patient be given information? Usually, because doctors and nurses did not believe he was in any position or condition to understand his own ailment. Nurses should not really be blamed for their refusal to tell patients their temperatures, pulse rates, blood pressure, or the nature of their medication. It was considered to be unethical for the nurses to talk to patients about their illnesses. This was a part of the practice of medicine.

What the patient does not realize is that although the hospital may seem impersonal, hundreds on the hospital team are working around the clock to give as professional care as they know how.

Patients, once past their particular crises, often are irritated by aspects of their care.

Why, some ask, is the food always cold? It is not, of course. The quality—whether it is good, and whether it is hot—of the food in hospitals depends on the particular hospital.

In Yale-New Haven Hospital, with its 750 beds, running sometimes at close to 90 percent occupancy, cooks prepare meals for some 675 patients, plus all the personnel in the hospital at meal time. Since the hospital employs some 2,100 people, this can be a great load. If one considers the number of special diets that mean individual cooking for any one meal, then it becomes apparent that Yale-New

Haven's kitchen runs like the kitchen of a luxury hotel, and has the same problems. The Yale-New Haven hospital complex covers several square blocks. The kitchen facilities have been located in the modern part of the hospital, where all meals are cooked. They are taken in heated and insulated trucks to the furthest reaches of the hospital. There they are reheated in individual floor kitchen units, and served. Closed dishes and thermal appliances are used.

The food that goes into Yale-New Haven or any other first-class hospital is probably better selected, more carefully purchased, and better in quality than in any but the most expensive restaurants. No hospital can afford to have anything but fresh, wholesome food. (If there is mold on the bread on your tray, look out for everything else in your hospital.)

Unlike first-class hotels, hospital kitchens are run by dieticians, and most of these are women. Forget the behemoth hospital such as Yale-New Haven for a moment, and consider the kitchen and feeding problems of a hospital that is much more of a size with the average American community hospital, Mary Hitchcock Hospital in Hanover, New Hampshire.

In 1965 Miss Dorothea Bartlett was chief dietician at Mary Hitchcock. She was responsible for the serving of 300 patient meals three times each day, plus an employee cafeteria which served 650 at lunch, and 250 every day at breakfast and dinner. In addition, Mary Hitchcock had a snack bar and various vending machines for the hungry personnel.

Like so many other successful modern hospitals, Mary Hitchcock had grown in bits and pieces. The original building was erected in 1893. New portions had come from time to time since then, and the hospital board was eager to build a six million dollar addition, for which it must raise $2,800,000—much of the rest would come from federal matching funds under the Hill-Burton program.

In 1965, Miss Bartlett's empire sprawled over a good city block and the hospital facilities even spanned the street to connect with another building. From the central kitchen it was possible to give good service to about half the patients. The others must be served from six pantries located strategically around the hospital.

The whole feeding operation emanated from the main kitchen. It began very early in the morning hours, when the stoves were heated and the planning, done long before, was consulted for the morning menu.

Mary Hitchcock Hospital at one time belonged to a central purchasing group which bought for several hospitals, but this group disbanded after a time. In 1965 Miss Bartlett bought largely from the Swift and Armour packing company distributing points close by. Twice a week a produce man came around with a truck of fresh fruits and vegetables.

In 1965 Mary Hitchcock Hospital made use of considerable quantities of frozen foods, which are easy to store and can be purchased at leisure and when prices are low.

When meal time came to Mary Hitchcock Memorial Hospital in the new part of the building, served by the central serving kitchen, the modern central tray service went into motion. The trays were placed in a line on a moving belt and sent up to the floors four at a time, by two dumb-waiters. The trays were checked by dieticians before they were served, then they were served by nursing personnel. That took care of about 126 patients.

The remainder of the food was put into special hot and

cold compartments in special trucks and the trucks were dispatched to floor kitchens, which from Miss Bartlett's point of view were one minute or so away.

There the dieticians and their assistants prepared the food and put it on trays for the other 116 patients in Mary Hitchcock, the trays were labelled, and the nursing people delivered them. (Nursing people included nurses' aides.)

At no point in her hospital, said Miss Bartlett, was food on a tray for more than six minutes before it was delivered to the patient. That was the crucial time—those minutes when the food was on the patient's tray and undelivered. Food could be kept hot and cold by various means as long as it remained in bulk. Once it went on the tray, the dieticians lost control of it thermally.

As for special diets, the floor kitchens in Mary Hitchcock Hospital had facilities for patients to make their own coffee. Meats could be broiled there, eggs could be cooked, and other foods could be specially prepared.

Dietician Bartlett had one ambition: to have complete control of the feeding of her patients. She did not then have it, because nursing personnel delivered some of the trays. This state of affairs existed at Mary Hitchcock because doctors there liked to know how their patients were eating, and they found the most reliable method was to have the nursing department responsible for food delivery. In other hospitals, the dietary department had this responsibility.

As far as hot food was concerned, there was one remarkable development in hospitals in the middle 1960's. That was the Pellett system of food service, which was used at a number of hospitals, including New York's Presbyterian Hospital, a 1,560 bed institution which had its share of problems in feeding patients. The Pellett system involved the use of an oven on an assembly line, with a carborundum disk holding the food plate inside a container. This made the crockery so hot the operators of the system must wear gloves, but it had made it possible to keep food hot for 20 minutes, which was a very long time.

Miss Bartlett, an indefatigable student of the food systems of other hospitals, traveled from Hanover to New York City one day in the summer of 1964 to see how this large hospital operated. She observed the Pellett system in action, and she also talked at length with the Presbyterian Hospital dietician. When they came into the kitchen, that dietician picked up a paper cup of ice cream from a counter and held it in her hand as they talked. They conversed for about 20 minutes. At the end of that time the other dietician gave the cup of ice cream to Miss Bartlett to examine for thermal properties. The ice cream was just beginning to melt away from the edges of the cup. The remainder was firm and cold.

The secret: two paper cups, one in which the ice cream was frozen nested inside another, acted much as does a thermos bottle and maintained a partial vacuum, keeping the ice cream cold long enough for delivery to a patient.

Such tricks were a part of the dietician's daily work at the hospitals, and where they know their business, the food was more than passable.

Some people, of course, said that hospital food was never that, but surprisingly enough, in spite of the cocktail conversation that almost universally condemned hospital food, there was not too much complaint in the better-run hospitals. Francis C. Houghton, administrator at Rutland's new hospital, said his hospital gave an appraisal card to every departing patient. In one three-month period, with more than six hundred answers, all but a half dozen responses were favorable about the general conduct of the hospital, and those that were unfavorable did not once mention the food negatively, although one question was devoted to the food.

"I didn't come to the hospital to eat," was one salty Vermonter's reply.

Another complaint of patients in the hospitals concerned wake-up time.

Why, asked many patients, did the patient have to be awakened at five o'clock in the morning?

The answer lay in the kitchen. The patient must get up and have his bath, get his teeth brushed, and be ready, because three meals had to be served to him in just as close to eight hours as is humanly possible.

In most hospitals the nurse or her aide came in the grim hours before the dawn, shaking thermometers and clanking urinals. The patient must be roused, washed, changed, patted, cranked up, fed, cleaned off, and ready when the doctor came.

The early wake-up of patients was the responsibility of the hospital administrator, one of whose jobs was to run the hospital in the interest of the patients.

The early wake-ups and wash-ups were also partly caused by the three-shift nursing system, which ran 8:00-4:00, 4:00-12:00, and 12:00-8:00. The night nurse had a relatively easy time, barring emergencies, until near the end of her shift. Then she must prepare the patients to face the day, and have it done before her shift ended. This meant wake-ups, temperatures, pulses, bedpans, medication, tooth brushing, face washing, and preparation for breakfast. If she worked in a hospital where the nurses served breakfast, she might also be involved in the breakfast detail. All this because the day shift nurses were going to be wanted by the doctors for assistance and consultation, and during those daylight hours of 8:00 to 4:00 the nurses had many different duties. In recent years hospital administrators had begun to question these old practices. In several New York hospitals wake-up times were made later than in yesteryear; sometimes the patients in wards were allowed to sleep until 6:30 in the morning, and private room patients were allowed nearly as much sleeping time as they could get.

To understand the wake-up time in a different sense, one must consider other hospital problems. The hospital could be said to be in full function only during the normal working hours of eight or nine in the morning to five or six in the evening. This was when the pharmacists and the X-ray departments and the physiotherapists and the laboratories were in full operation. If lab tests were to be made, the patient must supply the blood or the urine or the sputum or other substance, and the tests must be made by the technicians. No hospital ran its technical resources on an around-the-clock basis. In addition to the problem of feeding patients and taking their temperatures, the hospitals pleaded that they must backtime from the normal "business hours" when the special forces were in operation. This was a fair argument. The problem of the wake-up time seemed to be a problem more talked about than real.

What the patients thought of hospitals could often be determined by their responses to hospital "gripe sheets." Many hospitals gave their patients these sheets with general questions about the service, the food, and other conditions. St. Vincent's Hospital of New York City put out one "gripe sheet" which contained three different questions about nurses.

Changes were coming everywhere in hospital care.

Many of them were dictated by discoveries in medicine, such as a recent one at Columbia University-Presbyterian Hospital Medical Center in New York.

It was found that patients recovering from open heart surgery were likely to recover much more satisfactorily if they were permitted uninterrupted sleep, and if when awake they were given diversions, such as individual radio and television sets.

Diversions also seem to help children in hospitals. In Norwalk Hospital in Connecticut, a traveling zoo visited the children's unit, bringing skunks and guinea pigs and a snake named Longfellow.

The care of the patient, and the patient's reaction to such care, depended on the individual hospital. The best hospitals offered the finest; others had a long way to go to approximate the service of the best.

Chapter Twelve

THE PATIENT IN
THE HOSPITAL—II

Patients who enter the finest accredited American hospitals need not be alarmed by reports of accidents and malpractice in hospitals, for these occurrences are rare in well-regulated hospitals. However, malpractice does exist in our hospitals to a degree that is becoming alarming to health specialists. Dr. Robert C. Derbyshire, writing in the *Journal of the American Medical Association* in December, 1965, warned that although incompetent physicians constitute only a small minority of the medical profession, they could be a disproportionately large danger. He urged the staffs of accredited hospitals to assume more responsibility in dealing with incompetent physicians. Incompetent physicians are not the only dangers to the patient in the hospital. Incompetence or carelessness by *any* hospital employee can endanger the health or well-being of a patient.

One day in September, 1958, two patients were taken on wheeled stretchers from their rooms in a Chattanooga hospital to the surgical section of the hospital. An orderly wheeled one man out of his room into the hall, stopped, and went to a nearby room to wheel the other man out. Another orderly walked to the nursing station on the floor and picked up the two charts that belonged to the patients. The second orderly slipped one chart underneath the head of each patient, and then the two orderlies took their charges to the operating rooms. The charts identified the patients and specified the operation. One had come to the hospital for a hemorrhoidectomy. The other had come for a hernia operation and the removal of a cancerous testicle.

The orderlies delivered the patients to separate operating rooms. In each operating room the chart was checked, and the surgery began. In both cases the surgery was successful and uneventful. Only when the operations were completed did the horrified nurses learn that the charts had been switched, and so had the operations.

For the patient who had undergone the unnecessary and unwanted orchidectomy and hernia operation there was nothing to be done. The surgeons could not go back. The patient sued and was awarded $100,000.

How had the mix-up occurred? A nurse, not an orderly, should have checked patients and charts. A nurse, not an orderly, should have identified each patient with a wristband which would give the patient's vital hospital statistics and his name and the description of the operation. This was the practice in the best hospitals in the nation in 1958. But this Chattanooga hospital used wristbands only to identify newborn babies until this accident caused the hospital administration to bring its policies up to date.

This was malpractice. More malpractice suits are brought against doctors and hospitals each year than the year before, and in 1965 more than 10,000 such suits were taken to court. Medical and hospital authorities devoted conference after conference to the subject. Dr. Morris Fishbein devoted a column to it in *Medical World News* that summer. Damage awards handed down in malpractice cases were higher than ever before in history; in a Maryland case in 1964 the patient was awarded more than a million dollars, and in 1965 in Connecticut alone two different suits were filed asking totals of $3,500,000 each.

Malpractice includes anything and everything which might hurt the patient in the hospital, from not guarding against the patient's own wilfulness which causes him to fall out of bed, to the error of an unskilled surgeon.

One malpractice case involved a five-month-old baby who had been severely burned when a vaporizer upset in her family's home. The child was admitted to Woodlawn Hospital, a community hospital in Chicago. Then the hospital authorities discovered that her mother did not have Blue Cross or any other hospital insurance, nor did she have a $100 deposit, which the hospital demanded to assure payment of its bill. The mother was directed to take her baby to Cook County Hospital, where the poor of Chicago are treated without charge. Fourteen hours after the baby was taken into Cook County Hospital, she died. No autopsy was performed, and the cause of death was never precisely determined. The mother said the child died from neglect by the medical and hospital people of Woodlawn Hospital. The Chicago Board of Health, Cook County's coroner, and Mayor Kennelly of Chicago all began to investigate, and so did the newspapers. Woodlawn Hospital was cited for two violations of the law: failure to notify the police of an accident, and failure to have a licensed physician in attendance on the child. (She had been treated at Woodlawn by an intern.)

In this case the fault did not lie with any one doctor or nurse, or even with the administrator of the hospital, but in the growing practice of community hospitals to try to solve their problems of ever-increasing costs by neatly pigeonholing patients into financial categories. In the middle of the twentieth century most states, cities, and counties maintained tax-supported hospitals for the poor, but the burned baby's mother did not know that she should take her child to the county hospital, and not a community hospital.

Much more serious as malpractice are the cases in which there is bungling by licensed physicians in hospitals. One of these involved one of the largest malpractice jury awards in history. It occurred in California in 1962. A father was driving the family car and was forced to stop suddenly. A six-weeks-old baby in the car was thrown from his baby seat against the dashboard. He seemed to be hurt, and the father rushed him to the family doctor, who sent him to a hospital to consult a pediatrician.

At the hospital, the child was X-rayed. The pictures showed a skull fracture that extended almost from ear to ear. There was also evidence of bleeding inside the skull.

The baby was examined by a neurosurgeon, but for three days after admission to the hospital was not given blood transfusions or intravenous fluids. The baby would not eat and became dehydrated.

Later, blood transfusions were ordered, but then there was a mix-up in transfusion. The baby's blood was Type A negative, and he received Type A positive blood, not once, but twice. The child developed gangrene of the legs. Both legs were amputated below the knee on the fifth day in the hospital.

The child continued to be kept in the hospital for nearly eight months, suffering almost constantly from vomiting. Finally he was discharged, although he vomited twice on the day of discharge.

Eventually this child was taken to San Diego County General Hospital. It was discovered that bloody fluid was creating pressure on his brain. An operation was performed and the pressure was relieved, but the damage had been done. The child was mentally retarded thereafter and spastic on one side; his vision and hearing were impaired. He would have to remain in an institution for the rest of his life.

In another incident, a nine-year-old boy was taken to the operating room of a Dallas hospital for a simple adenoid operation. The anesthesia was given by a nurse-anesthetist, as was usual there, and the operation began. Suddenly there was an explosion and fire in the anesthetic machine. The boy inhaled flames into his lungs, and died a few hours later.

In this case a jury decided that the nurse-anesthetist had been negligent in using the equipment. This was a failure by the trained practitioners of the healing arts to protect the patient from harm.

In another malpractice case, the family of a Seattle mason was awarded nearly $450,000. He had been working on a scaffold at the eighth floor of a Seattle hospital when he slipped and fell 112 feet to the ground, suffering internal injuries and a fractured left hip. Several weeks later, when the hip fracture refused to heal, a resident orthopedic surgeon in the hospital secured the patient's consent to do surgery. There were definite indications that the man's heart was not all it should be, but the operation

was done, nonetheless. On the operating table the patient's heart stopped. After 35 minutes of closed-chest
heart massage the heart began beating again, but the
stoppage had been far too long. The patient was crippled,
and would be confined to a nursing home under constant
care for the rest of his life.

The point here was not that the surgeon erred in doing
closed heart massage when he should have done open
heart massage (although that came out at the trial). The
point was that this man had signed a release for surgery,
but it had not been an *informed release*. In other words,
the hospital authorities had not told him that the surgery
was *elective*—that is, it could wait. They had not told him
that considering the condition of his heart the surgery
would be dangerous to him at best.

In another case, a patient entered a Veteran's Administration hospital in Maryland for an operation on his lungs
in 1959. He had contracted tuberculosis of the lungs during his military service, and the operation was to remove
a part of the right lung. This was done. Later it was decided that another operation must be performed. As a
training matter, the hospital's chief surgical resident was
chosen to do the surgery. His assistant, and the man who
would watch carefully over every move of this young doctor, was to be the hospital's chief of surgery.

The surgeon began the operation. During the course of
it, while the chief surgeon was out of the operating room,
he encountered difficulties which he did not completely
understand, and he put gauze packs in a space between
the ribs to stop bleeding. In doing so he caused pressure
to be exerted on the spinal column. The result was
paralysis of the lower limbs of the patient.

The disaster might never have occurred had the surgeon

in charge not become careless or overconfident and deserted the operating room at a critical moment.

Malpractice may also be the result of poor or careless hospital service by non-professional employees—sometimes not even hospital employees but service personnel from outside.

In 1958, in Connecticut, a 42-year-old chauffeur was admitted to a hospital for a gall bladder operation. The operation was successful, and the patient was taken from the operating room while still under the anesthetic to be wheeled back to his own room. He was wheeled to the elevator and the doors opened.

Suddenly, when the stretcher was halfway in and halfway out of the elevator, the car began to move upward, doors still open. Those in the elevator and near it watched in horror as the stretcher canted upward, to stop only when the unconscious patient's chest was wedged between elevator car and the metal coaming of the door. The patient died of a crushed chest, without ever coming out of the anesthetic.

The elevator, the hospital administrator discovered, had broken down earlier in the day, but repairmen had come to fix it, and it had been working properly up to the moment of the accident.

The above are cases of accidents, carelessness, and even incompetence in the healing arts. These problems have always existed. Why, then, was the number of malpractice suits in the 1960's growing every year to beleaguer those engaged in health care in America?

One reason was a change in legal philosophy with the result that in the middle of the twentieth century nearly all hospitals lost their immunity from suit. In earlier times the hospital could not be sued because the law said it was a dispenser of charity. In 1965 fewer than half a dozen of the fifty states retained laws giving charitable immunity to hospitals.

Doctors have had some relief in the past few years from a certain unfair and vexing type of malpractice threat. Until the 1960's there was a growing tendency for victims of accidents to sue doctors who stopped at the scene to treat the injured. By 1965, 40 states had passed "Good Samaritan laws" which specifically protect doctors from malpractice suits for rendering first aid at an accident.

Another reason for the growth of malpractice suits in America was the decreasing respect in which the public held practitioners of the healing arts. In earlier times the doctor was beloved by society, and the hospital did not take so active a part in the healing process. In the 1960's the medical profession's prestige had sunk as doctors led in the resistance to social change. As the hospitals took more responsibility for the public health they also assumed more liability.

Some hospitals in 1965 displayed an odd way of looking at accidents. If the accident was not reported to the press, and there was no trouble, many hospitals did not call it an accident at all, but an "incident." An incident, then, was an accident that did not bring about unfavorable publicity or a damage suit.

It was not particularly difficult for the general public to sense this attitude by hospital administrators and other staff members, so some Americans began to believe that what happened in the hospitals was covered up by hospital employees, nurses, and doctors. There was some truth to this charge, although not as much as there once was. Asked how he protected his hospital against lawsuits, one administrator said, "We are protected by malpractice insurance, and also make sure that no medical information gets into the hands of unauthorized persons. No lawsuits pending."

This represented an aspect of the notorious "conspiracy of silence" with which the health professions had long been charged. This "conspiracy" was breaking down in the middle 1960's, as the 10,000 malpractice suits of 1965 indicated. Once it was difficult for lawyers to find doctors who would testify against other doctors in malpractice suits. Not in the 1960's. In one case several doctors on the staff of a hospital testified against that hospital in a malpractice suit, and in another case an insurance company brought suit against an intern who had been on the staff of an Oregon hospital and was accused of causing a malpractice suit for which the insurance company had to pay damages. In yet another strange twist of malpractice, a Virginia physician sued an insurance company successfully for ignoring an opportunity to settle a malpractice case out of court in 1965, just before it went to trial.

One West Virginia administrator reported serious malpractice problems. In this particular hospital there was an accident every week, he said. Patients fell out of bed, or they fell out of wheelchairs. The nurses had been cautioned there to back down ramps with patients in wheelchairs, for there had been many accidents when a patient lost control and ended up in a heap at the bottom, wheelchair on top of him.

Some such accidents were obviously the fault of patients, as those who tried to walk against the orders of their doctors. In a Minnesota hospital a patient who was seriously ill decided that he was going to go home, although his doctor told him to stay in his bed in the hospital. When hospital employees saw the man get up and try to dress they put him in bed, and when he protested they restrained him with a device called a Posey belt, which kept him from getting out of bed.

The patient was still determined to leave. He found a knife and cut himself loose from the restraining belt. He climbed out a window while the private nurse who was assigned to him was outside the room picking up medicines. His room was on the second floor, and when he jumped down he injured his foot. He sued the hospital for negligence, and collected $6,500.

Was the hospital really guilty of negligence? This sort of award led hospital administrators to throw up their hands in dismay.

In a Mississippi hospital a man who was admitted for concussion seemed to be lucid, so no guardrails were put around his bed. He rang for a nurse. Thirty minutes went by, he said, and no nurse came, so he got up to go to a bathroom. He fell on his head. He sued the hospital.

In Idaho, a tuberculosis patient suddenly sat up on the side of her bed and rang for assistance. A passing nurse saw her and told her to sit still, she would return in a moment. Before she could return, the patient got up to walk, fell, and fractured a hip.

In upstate New York, a laboratory worker in a state hospital fell ill one day at work and visited the hospital infirmary. She was being taken into an ambulance when the stretcher on which she was riding fell apart and dumped her to the ground. She sued and collected damages because the court said the hospital was negligent.

In Minnesota an 86-year-old patient in a county hospital fell off a portable toilet and fractured his hip. He sued, and he collected.

A nurse in Delaware gave a patient two injections in the

buttock, damaging the sciatic nerve and causing permanent damage to his leg. He sued and won.

What are hospitals to do? one administrator asked. Should they put all patients in straitjackets? Should they keep nurses on special duty at all times? Side rails were one apparent answer, but if a patient was determined to climb out of bed, one administrator said, the side rails just gave them farther to fall.

There were accidents that did not involve bad medical or nursing care. In one hospital, a patient suddenly clamped his jaws down on a thermometer, bit it in half, and swallowed half of it. That certainly was an accident, which no one could have avoided except the patient.

One Kentucky hospital reported all these accidents in 1965:

—An 80-year-old visitor slipped on the highly waxed floor of the hospital, broke her hip, and died.

—A 38-year-old woman was burned by a wire that led to the light over her bed.

—A 40-year-old woman fell when the panel of a table on which she was leaning slipped suddenly, and she broke her arm.

—A woman visitor was bitten by a bat that flew through a broken screen.

Hospitals seem to be like people. Some are accident-prone and others are not.

Hospitals try to protect themselves against lawsuits with malpractice insurance purchased from commercial insurance companies. A decade ago a policy of $500,000 was considered to be a large malpractice policy, but in 1965 suits had reached seven times that figure. Not all hospitals either chose to get or could get malpractice insurance. In Utah one group of more than 15 hospitals banded together to insure one another, and so did several hospitals in Alaska, where there was much litigation. One Alaska hospital of 150 beds reported more than a dozen suits pending in the spring of 1965.

A few American hospitals were brave enough or rash enough not to carry malpractice insurance at all. One, in Vermont, carried no insurance because "premiums are too high, and it is felt that we can do better without." This hospital board was content to report all accidents and unusual occurrences to its attorneys.

"The best protection against suits," the administrator of another Vermont hospital said, "is to do everything to protect the patient that can be done. For example, we have had no bed accidents since going to all-electric beds (which are lowered and raised gently through electronic controls). Many before. . . . All suits come from either inadequate equipment or people doing something wrong."

Another simple safeguard against potential lawsuits was described by a Nevada hospital administrator.

A diabetic patient had come in to have a leg cast removed. While removing the cast, the technician accidentally scratched the patient's leg in two small areas. He made no report of this to the hospital, and the patient went home. Her diabetes went out of control because of infection, and soon she returned to the hospital with two large ulcers on her leg. The hospital did not argue about who was negligent and who was not, but put the patient to bed, cared for her diabetes and brought it under control, cured her ulcers, and discharged her. The patient was grateful for the care which was given at no charge to her, and no lawsuit was brought or even considered.

Nevertheless, distrust between patient and hospital often existed, and too often it was mutual distrust. In one

Alaska hospital the administrator in 1965 alerted his staff
to "perpetrated accidents." That hospital's employees took
away from the patients anything such as hypodermic
needles, "which they can use for evidence for some story
they may concoct."

There were ways to keep accidents under control. One
way was the maintenance of safety committees which
meet regularly, discuss service problems, and invite insurance company specialists and other experts to inspect
the premises.

Suits against hospitals often were caused by fear, or the
certainty in the patient's mind that he was being neglected. In 1965 many patients knew, and doctors were beginning to understand that they knew, much of what
was not told them. That year, writing in *GP*, a magazine for the general practitioner of medicine, Dr. James
R. Nichols noted that a twelve-year-old girl with an in-
operable brain tumor learned that she had cancer and that
she was going to die, although everyone around her tried
to keep the information from her. They tried too hard.
She guessed, she said, because she noticed that her father
and mother had suddenly begun going to church more
than usual. Dr. Nichols said that after a doctor makes
diagnosis of a fatal disease, it could be assumed that in
five days or less somehow the patient would know about
it.

The patient who knows that his doctor is keeping something important from him loses confidence in the doctor.
Exactly the same thing happens when the nurses or the
hospital conceal information, as may be seen in one man's
story of his loss of regard for a Colorado general hospital.

A man was involved in an automobile accident on January 12, 1965, at eight o'clock in the morning. He was

taken by ambulance to a city-county institution. He was admitted at around nine o'clock. He waited nearly an hour for examination. He had a wound on the side of his head, but it was not stitched there, although later, when he was transferred to a military hospital, it required four stitches.

He said he was kept lying on an examination table for six hours without an explanation. His wound was not cleansed and no X-rays were taken, nor was any bandage placed around his head. Finally, at 2:30 in the afternoon, he was placed in an ambulance and sent to the military hospital. Still he was told nothing.

Afterwards, he became indignant and wrote a letter to the editor of a local newspaper regarding what he said was neglect and maltreatment. The editors of the paper sent a copy of the letter to the city manager of the Department of Health and Hospitals. The manager talked to hospital authorities, and then replied. Here is the way the case looked to the hospital:

The patient was admitted at about nine in the morning and was placed on a wooden back-board for an examination, because he might have a back injury. He was examined and his injuries were found to be minor. The police had placed a "hold" order on the man, which meant the hospital was to hold him until further notice. This was common police procedure, and it did not mean that the patient had done anything wrong, only that the police investigation of the accident had not been completed. Efforts were made by the hospital as the hours went by to get in touch with the police, but there was some difficulty in reaching those with authority to release the hold order.

No X-rays were taken at this hospital because the patient said he wanted to be transferred, and it was policy not to take X-rays under such conditions. A call was put in to the military hospital for an ambulance, but it did not arrive for some time.

The director said he was quite satisfied that the patient had received the best of attention. The trouble was, from the patient's point of view, that no one told *him* any of the procedure or the reasons for the action that were taken, and he believed all the time that he was being neglected.

There was one type of malpractice, the most worrisome of all, which was responsible for many injuries and deaths. It was illustrated by a case that occurred in 1958 in a well-to-do community on Long Island.

A ten-year-old boy was brought to the hospital to have his tonsils taken out. In the operating room he was attended by a surgeon and an anesthesiologist, who administered the anesthetic. After the successful operation the boy was taken into the recovery room, just off the operating room. He was still unconscious, but seemed to be in good condition. Neither the surgeon nor the anesthesiologist remained with the boy. They left him in the charge of the nurse in the recovery room.

The nurse was new to the recovery room. She was busy with other work, and did not notice for some time that the boy was in trouble. His heart had stopped. It was several minutes, apparently, before she saw this. She called a surgeon from the adjoining operating room. After a minute and twenty seconds of cardiac massage the boy's heart began beating again. But the boy's brain had been without oxygen for too long and brain damage was the result. The boy became a permanent invalid with cerebral palsy, mental retardation, and nearly total loss of vision.

In the lawsuit that was brought by the boy's family it was charged that both doctors and hospital were responsible. The hospital had not maintained a proper recovery room, it was said, and had not enforced proper rules for surgical procedure. The doctors had abandoned their patient.

The standards of the Mayo and Lahey Clinics were cited. There, strict rules dictated that surgeon and anesthesiologist personally wheel the patient into the recovery room and stay with him until the patient can feel pain. At those institutions, because of this practice, cardiac arrest was virtually unheard of.

This practice was not confined to the Lahey and Mayo Clinics. It was expected practice at all hospitals accredited by the Joint Commission on Hospital Accreditation.

Chapter Thirteen

WHO PAYS
FOR WHAT?

When the average American entered the hospital in 1966 he was probably too sick or too frightened to worry much about what his stay was going to cost, but at some time while he was in the hospital the thought began to nag at him. If he was lucky and had full Blue Cross coverage, the cost to him might not be very high. It might be nothing at all. If he had only partial Blue Cross coverage, partial commercial coverage, or none at all, then the costs could be staggering.

Much depended on where the American lived, in north, south, east or west, in country or in city. It depended on what kind of hospital he was in, and what kind of care he needed or someone wanted for him. At New York City's New York Hospital, one of the most expensive in America, he might pay $38 a day if he was in a four-bed ward. This included board and room, and normal nursing and care services. If he wanted or needed a private room, and nurses around the clock, then the cost would rise to about $130 a day—$60 for the room and board, and about $70 a day for nurses. That was at New York Hospital. If he was in some other hospital in that city, one of the small ones, or in a rural area where the nursing problem was acute, he might not be able to get around-the-clock nursing service.

In a county hospital in Nebraska, he would pay $11 for a ward bed, $12-14 for a semi-private room, and $16 for a private room. In comparison to New York, on the basis of cost alone, it seems quite a bargain.

Costs of hospitalization were very high on the West Coast, partly because labor costs were high. In 1965 the cost of a day of hospitalization there was estimated by the American Hospital Association to be $54.28, while in the deep South it was only $34.31. The New York area was put at $43.03.

Those figures refer to overall cost, and in this the room rates or bed rates could be deceptive. Also, where hospitals changed to accommodate the public taste, or the taste of architects and administrators, the expenses rose. It cost money to have wall-to-wall carpeting in lobbies and in rooms. It cost money to have Siamese silk drapes rather than starched cotton curtains.

What goes into these costs, and why were they so high and rising?

Look at some of the factors.

A hospital in Illinois lost an average of $80 on every maternity case, $20 on every major operation, $9 on every minor operation, and $28 on every patient who was given occupational therapy. How did that hospital make up the losses? By charging far above cost for laboratory tests, drug prescriptions, X-ray services, private rooms, and bed and board.

To be specific about hospital costs, take the case of a

woman who entered a hospital in Connecticut in 1964, suffering from a heart infection. She was put into a four-bed room. Once this would have been called a ward, but no longer. The service was exactly the same as it would have been in a two-bed, semi-private room. The difference was that her charges for room and board were $20 per day; in the semi-private room they would have been $24, using the old standard of two persons to a semi-private room. She was in the hospital for 108 days, and her total bill was $2,300, of which $2,150 was for room and board, nursing, and all the other services of the hospital. Basically, this woman was paying $20 a day for hotel and nursing service while she recovered from this infection under the care of her physician. This represents the old concept of the hospital as a hotel for the sick. She had a few laboratory tests, costing less than $50 in all, and the other $100 went for medicine, for which this particular hospital charges at a rate just slightly higher than cost.

Another case history in which the same hospital was used in a different way concerned a man who was admitted with a kidney disease. He spent only six weeks in the hospital, less than half the time of the lady with the heart infection, yet his bill was $200 higher. Why? He had a semi-private (two-person) room at $24 a day. The huge difference, however, was in the use of the laboratory. The bill for laboratory tests, X-rays, and blood transfusions came to about $1,000. He also paid heavily for the overall costs of the hospital, because this hospital was one of those that used its laboratory charges to help make up deficits in other departments. Its laboratory costs were among the highest in the state of Connecticut.

Every patient who came into this hospital was given three laboratory tests: a blood count, a urinalysis, and a test for venereal disease. All in all, this hospital offered some 225 different laboratory tests, ranging from $1 to $30 in cost. Every one contained a hidden charge to help cover losses in other hospital services.

One point of loss was the emergency room, and this was true of every hospital that offered emergency services to its community. In another Connecticut town a city visitor stubbed his toe on the diving board at his wealthy friend's house one warm summer day, then rushed to the hospital's emergency room for treatment. He complained because he was forced to wait an hour, and went away after having medication and dressing applied to his aching toe. He never did pay the $10 bill sent to him by the hospital for the use of its emergency room and the dressings. He was not atypical. This hospital in 1962-63 showed figures of about $6,000 in expense attributable directly to the operation of that hospital's emergency room, and about $13,000 in income from the emergency room. But it was a fantasy —that income figure—because almost half of the emergency room's income was never collected. This was typical; in a check by the Illinois Hospital Association in 1964 the Chicago hospitals reported that they failed to collect between a third and a half of their emergency room billings.

Connecticut towns and Chicago were alike in one respect, their bad debts were made good by the paying patients, either personally or through insurance policies. The lady with the heart infection and the man with the kidney infection both paid the bills of people with cuts or bruises who came to the hospital emergency room. The unfortunate and unfair part, from the standpoint of the average American patient, was that the bill of the poor man and

the bill of the rich man were almost the same, and both
are charged equally for the losses of the hospital.

Whether they paid equally or not, and how the bills
were paid, will be dealt with in Chapter Fourteen. What
affected the patient was the fact that from his point of
view the hospital's accounting system had become a hopeless jumble, and it did not represent in any way the actual
costs of providing the services involved, for somewhere in
every patient's bill was a little piece of the salary of the
nurse trainees, the cost of the electric typewriter in the
administrator's office, the big city banker's unpaid emergency-room bill, and the subscription to *Life* in the car-
peted floor of the lobby.

In the aggregate, this may all seem fair to the hospital
administrators and the insuring companies who caused
them to change their system of accounting. Some patients,
like the lady with the heart infection, received bargains
in their hospital care. A person who had kidney problems
and needed regular kidney dialysis, which is a cleansing
of the blood, would be charged for his hospital care on the
basis of the use of the equipment. If he was a charity patient, and the cost over a year for dialysis was $10,000, as
it very well might be, who was going to pay that cost?
Everyone who paid a hospital bill in that particular hospital would pay a portion of it.

John M. Danielson, president of the Illinois Hospital
Association, said in 1965 that the bills could be cut drastically if hospitals charged the average American only for
the care he received.[1] His charge was not so much a complaint about the incompetence of hospital administrators
as a plea for the relief of patients, for letting the charges
for services not rendered them be paid by somebody else.

Averaging out, using the various profit-making departments to pay for the losses of such departments as the
emergency room, is an accountants' device. For a patient
who came into a hospital for surgery or normal medication, this might not be unfair. But in other cases it could
be most unfair and most expensive to the patient.

A prominent New York man incurred a hospital debt of
$30,000 after paying hospital bills of $24,000 over a two-
year period when his wife was stricken with ulcerative co-
litis.

Laboratory, X-ray, and pharmacy bills were the worst
of it. His wife went from one hospital to another—to seven
in all—seeking a cure of her disease. Sometimes the daily
pharmacy cost was $48, and at one hospital he discovered
that he was being charged $5 for the aspirin.

Some of his problems were aggravated by hospital practices. Several hospitals refused to release X-rays showing
the patient's condition at various times, because the doctors who were then treating the woman were not members
of the hospital staff. The man then spent several hundred
dollars for extra X-rays. Several hospitals refused to release records, or the patient's charts, for use by other doctors not on the hospital staff. All this meant multiplication
of expense running into thousands of dollars.

The voluntary hospital's defense of such practices sometimes was stated as the necessity to keep revenues high to
meet other known losses.

As people found hospital costs higher and harder to
meet, the hospitals suffered increasingly from non-pay-
ment of bills.

One Connecticut hospital showed accounts past due of
$145,000 in September, 1965, which represented more than
a month's total income. Fifteen years earlier that little

hospital was writing off as bad debts about one and a half percent of its total bills. In 1965 the amount written off had risen to five percent.

Verbal complaints about hospital bills were not as common as one might think. One administrator said this was because about eighty percent of patients were covered by some form of insurance, and the insurance companies paid the bills, or most of them.

Yet hospital bills could be disastrous for the two people in ten who had no insurance coverage, since the whole system of American hospitals had come to revolve around the insurance plans.

In the month of August, 1965, the board of trustees of another Connecticut hospital sat down to consider the problem of certain delinquent accounts. This was a regular function of the trustees, who decided which non-paying patients should be forgiven their debts, and which should be pursued, even to the courts, by the business office of the hospital.

Here were some typical cases:

—A man who had been in the hospital still owed $180 after eight months. He could not pay it. His wife had already auctioned off most of their worldly goods to pay back bills and live. At that moment this family needed financial aid.

—A man owed $163.75, which he had owed for a year. He had a nursery business and a large family, and he earned nothing in the winter.

—An old lady had died in the hospital, leaving a debt of $423.50. It would be paid out of the estate.

—A man refused to pay the $169.70 owed for delivery of a baby to his wife. It was not his baby, he said.

—A woman day-worker had a bill that was nearly a

year old. The bill was $1,139.85, and she stoutly insisted
that some day she would pay the bill in full. She was still
ill, and could not get back to work, but she was not a welfare case.

Hospital costs for some of these people, who never complained in a letter-to-the-editor, were absolutely disastrous. That much is apparent.

What was not readily apparent in hospital bills and in
discussions of costs, were some of the reasons for running
up hospital costs. A hospital in North Dakota installed all
the equipment necessary for open-heart surgery in 1965—
an outlay of money equal to about ten percent of all the
other physical assets of the hospital. This was not a teaching hospital, in the sense that it was not a university hospital, nor was it a medical center. The question might be
raised as to whether or not that hospital's patients should
pay for the expensive special equipment. As might be expected, this hospital's rates were considerably higher than
those of other hospitals in that general area.

There can be good reason for the establishment of expensive hospital facilities to serve specific purposes, as the
Shriners of the Masonic Order have shown. They built 17
hospitals in the United States to treat the crippling illnesses and accidents of children, and were particularly
noted for their "burn hospitals," which do what few other
hospitals could do in the treatment and rehabilitation of
burns that otherwise would cause loss of limbs or life. The
treatment of such burn cases might involve hospitalization for an entire year, at a cost of perhaps $12,000. This
cost could not be borne by many families, to say nothing
of the medical costs involved in operations, grafts, and
other treatment. The Shriners, not the general community,
bore this cost.

The Medicare program was bound to increase the cost of hospitalization to patients all along the line, by one provision of the law that concerned radiologists, physiatrists, anesthesiologists and pathologists. In 1966 they would begin to do their own billing and collecting from patients. They *must* do this in order to qualify under the Medicare program. What does it mean to the average American hospital patient who is not under Medicare?

The situation in one Connecticut hospital in 1965 was typical of a common method of compensation of specialists. Here the radiologist and pathologist worked directly in the hospital. Both used the hospital's equipment, and the pathologist was in charge of the laboratory and its technicians. Each received twelve percent of the hospital's billings for pathology and X-ray work. In the aggregate it came to a very satisfactory income for each man. The income was even higher if one considered the lack of expense in achieving it. The pathologist and radiologist did not send bills. They had no office expense. They had no typing expense, no bookkeeping expense, and no collections and bad debts expense. Under the new program these specialists would have all these expenses, and their charges to the hospital patients would reflect them. The charges were bound to rise considerably.

A bill for good hospitalization need not be any more than one for only fair hospitalization. This has been proved by the operations of the Mayo Clinic, one of the finest medical and surgical institutions in America, whose practices are often cited by the leaders in medicine and hospital care. In fact, the Mayo Clinic recently was shown to be first among 25 institutions listed most frequently as the place of residency by part-time teachers of medicine in the nation's medical schools. It is very, very good, and nothing more need be said. Mayo is not a hospital. It uses hospitals in its area. But this clinic provides many over-lapping services.

Mayo's fees were just about average for the country as a whole. This did not mean they compared with New York Hospital's bills, which were very high, or with Los Angeles County General's, which were relatively high for those who could pay. A three-day physical examination at Mayo, including all tests, cost between $125 and $225. There was nothing bargain-basement about Mayo's. There was no question about who got the good care, either. Some were referred to the clinic by other doctors. Some came to Rochester, Minnesota, without reference, certain that they would be taken. They were. There was no discrimination on the basis of race, color, creed, or financial condition. Indeed, no one was turned away and no one was ever asked about his financial condition until he had been discharged by his doctor. Then he was directed to the business office and he made his arrangements there.

In many hospitals, a very important factor in the pa-tient's bill was the failure of the various government agen-cies to pay enough for welfare and charity patients to meet the actual costs of the hospital. Government units usually made a per diem payment, and it might be as little as a quarter of the stated cost per day for keeping a patient in a hospital.[2] Who was to blame for this?

Many state, county, and city authorities claimed that the hospital accounting systems were so complex the charges meant nothing. Hospitals often claimed that gov-ernment agencies were taking a free ride at the expense of the hospitals. Nevertheless, a few states and government units paid the stated charges of the hospital without question. Vermont was one of these. Poor patients in Vermont hospitals, or Vermonters treated in neighboring New Hampshire, had their full bills paid by the state government. New Hampshire, on the other hand, made a flat per diem payment which did not cover the stated costs of the hospitals in practically any case, with the possible exception of chronic illness hospitals with their generally lower cost structures. New Hampshire's method of operation was much more common among the states than Vermont's.

Perhaps hospital costs could not be brought down in 1966, but as Administrator Danielson of Illinois indicated, certain inequities could be reduced.

Hospitals might decide to stop bearing the whole load for patients whose care should be a community responsibility. At one Connecticut hospital the welfare cases, or what should be welfare or charity cases, comprised perhaps ten percent of the total of patients. These came chiefly from New York and Connecticut. The two states used the same basic formula for reimbursing the hospital. That was about all they had in common in their attitude toward payment of hospitals. Both states paid slightly over $28 a day for nonmaternity cases, and $29.50 for maternity cases, plus $12.00 for the child when it was born. New York would pay the bills for unwed mothers, but Connecticut would not. Connecticut would pay for the aged, but not for young people in their 30's and 40's. The towns of Connecticut were supposed to pay these bills, but the town selectmen, conscious of the tax burden on the community, often refused to pay. New York was no more punctual. In one month, when the trustees of this hospital were considering how to handle old bills on which little or no payment would be made, they discovered that 85 percent of those bills represented New York State patients, most of whose bills should have been paid by some state or county agency.

The paying patients at this hospital in 1965 were carrying the tax burden for several state and local governments, and nearly everywhere that local hospitals took welfare patients this was the case.

Other cost factors that Mr. Danielson suggested could be eliminated from the patient's bill would be nurses' training, technicians' training, and the training of interns and resident physicians. These costs could be taken out of the hospital expenses and added then to the educational expenses of the community and the nation. As it was in 1965, people who paid hospital bills and medical insurance premiums were paying for this education. How much did it cost? That depended on the area and the extent of educational facilities. One administrator of a teaching hospital suggested that elimination of education would cut perhaps five dollars a day from the overall patient cost, and this could be returned directly to the patient or insurance premium payer.

Some strides had been made in the development of the progressive care program to cut the cost to the patient. Very seldom did a seriously ill patient have the three-shift, private nurse schedule any longer in an advanced hospital. He was put in the intensive care section, which cost perhaps half of the private-room, private-nurse program. He was moved then to the regular care section, and finally he might be moved to the minimal care section, where he might be up and around for a few days before going home.

The development of medical centers would also cut

costs; one hyperbaric oxygen chamber would be enough for a whole community, perhaps a whole state.

Costs could be cut, but they probably could not be cut very much in the twentieth-century society, and no matter how changes were made, the slack would soon be taken up by increasing wages and fees, since seventy percent of the cost of an American hospital represented pay to people who work there. Every raise in the state or federal minimum wage laws, and every gain in benefits made by an employee group, meant an increase in cost to the hospital. There did not seem to be any way of getting around this.

Chapter Fourteen

HOW THE HOSPITAL
GETS PAID

In 1965 if you wanted to find the Blue Cross offices in any big American city, you looked around for the biggest, tallest, newest skyscraper in town, and chances were that you found them right there. Probably it was called the Blue Cross-Blue Shield Building.

Blue Cross, with its 80 organizations and 60,000,000 subscribers in the United States, was one of the nation's most successful new industries. It paid its employees well, and it housed them during working hours in well-appointed offices. Like many of the other successful new American industries, Blue Cross was a non-profit bureaucracy. Like a government bureaucracy it drew its money by taxing the people. In 1964, 76 of the nation's 80 Blue Cross plans increased their tax on the American people in one way or another, and in the fall of 1965 the 77th plan, that of Northeast Ohio, asked the state insurance department for permission to boost its rates more than 18 per-

218

cent. Before the end of the year three new plans had come into existence. Hospital insurance, like other insurance, was regulated by insurance commissioners.

Blue Cross was the leading plan, and it was very good, particularly since profit-making was not in the picture. But it did share some of the attitudes of government bureaucracy: since Blue Cross can raise its "tax" on its subscribers at the will of insurance commissions, the charge was made that it was not as concerned with the costs of hospitals as a private company would be. Blue Cross officials often pointed to their low administrative cost (five percent or under on average) but a percentage figure, even a low one, can be misleading. For example, Henry Kaiser took shipbuilding contracts during World War II at his West Coast yards on a cost-plus-ten-percent basis, and made millions. Cost was no object in those days, the ships had to be built. That was the way it was in 1965 with hospital insurance. To be sure, Blue Cross ran surveys and checks on hospitals to examine their costs, but the net result of Blue Cross was to raise hospital expenses. A valid argument could be made that hospital expenses had to be raised. They were—with a vengeance. In the five years between 1959 and 1964 New York's Blue Cross raised its rates 124 percent.

Blue Cross was a *hospital* plan in every sense of the word. It was originated by hospitals in 1929, and it was still run by and for hospitals. In 1965 Blue Cross subscribers had no voice in the selection of any officials, and some of them were saying that this hospital control was a factor in the rising cost of hospital insurance as well as hospital bills. In New York City dissatisfaction grew to the point in 1964 where a new plan called Group Health Hospital

Insurance was formed to compete with Blue Cross, starting with a basis of 750,000 subscribers to the medical service it already had in competition with Blue Shield.

Some Americans preferred to carry other kinds of health insurance. It might be paid for by the company for which they worked. They might buy it privately. They might carry both Blue Cross and outside hospitalization insurance. Altogether 88,000,000 people had outside protection, and another 7,000,000 were covered by plans that were independent of Blue Cross and the insurance companies. In a quarter of a century the number of people protected by hospital programs rose from 12,000,000 to 145,000,000.

In all this time there was very little basic change in hospital insurance, or in any form of health insurance. With the coming of Medicare, insurance men and Blue Cross men expected a sharp change in insurance practices. The trend would be, they said, toward insurance that provided for fully paid hospital stays for younger people, like those the old people would have under Medicare, and for such benefits as nursing home care.

Some of the most serious problems of health insurance in the 1960's were substandard policies and frauds. The American Medical Association in 1965 began a drive to persuade insurance commissioners in the various states to crack down on shady health-insurance promoters. Earlier, Jack Owen, vice-president of the New Jersey Hospital Association, testified about bad practices before a United States Senate investigating committee. He told how a patient entered a hospital and told the admissions clerk that he was covered by one of the best-known insurance companies in the country. When it came to pay the bill, he and the hospital discovered that the policy he held was with a small, fly-by-night company with a name that sounded almost exactly like that of the large company. The hospital bill was $603, and this policy paid exactly $27 of it.

Many strange situations arise in the insurance field. One is the matter of duplicating insurance, which enables some patients to make a profit by being sick and in the hospital. Yale-New Haven Hospital made a study of several cases of this kind, showing just how much some people *earned* by staying in bed in the hospital.

One case was that of a man who had Blue Cross and a commercial insurance policy. He was in the hospital 40 days, and his bill was $6,717.35. Blue Cross paid $5,169.45. The commercial insurance paid $5,833.68. He received a refund from the hospital of $4,285.78, which meant that he was earning $107 per day all the time he was in the hospital.

Another case involved a man with Blue Cross and a labor-union insurance plan. His bill was $3,200. Blue Cross paid $2,400, the union insurance paid $2,300, and the man received a rebate of some $1,500, or $64 per day.

One lady who had two Blue Cross policies (she was also covered under her husband's policy) discovered that the total hospital bill of $709.55 was paid by one policy, and she received a rebate from the other of exactly that amount. In 1965, after studying a number of such cases, Blue Cross officials around the country began to move to eliminate the duplication of payments under two Blue Cross plans, but for persons who carried both Blue Cross and commercial insurance, it was and would be possible to make illness "profitable."

Elsewhere in this book some practices of the proprietary hospitals have been mentioned, but where the proprietary hospitals were most vulnerable to criticism was in the matter of charges. The situation in California, although exaggerated beyond that of other areas, proved the point.

In Southern California there were some three hundred hospitals, and more of these fell into the proprietary than in any other category. There were reasons for this phenomenon in California, as mentioned; one was the massive increase of population in California in the years since the end of World War II. Another was the practice of builders in California of promising that their developments would contain schools, shopping centers, medical offices, *and hospitals*. Doctors and other groups were persuaded to form hospital corporations and build hospitals.

To some extent the growth of hospitals-for-profit met a real need, but some strange practices came into being in the middle 1950's, when the percentage of proprietary to non-profit hospitals was at its highest nationally, and California's profit-making hospitals were increasing faster than those of any state.

These hospitals soon found themselves in a price war. What did they do? They did just what supermarkets do, they offered loss leaders and made up the difference in other charges. The loss leaders were the standard expenses, such as room and board.

There was a good reason for this loss-leader plan. Commercial insurance policies usually stipulated that they would pay only so much, in dollars and cents, for rooms. They were much less specific about other services. So the charges of "other services" became the important charges. Patients were charged twenty-five cents for a tongue depressor; $1 for the use of a patient gown, $5 for a common sitz-bath for which other hospitals charged nothing; $3 for proctoscope rental, when other hospitals charged nothing;

$5 as a recording fee, for the keeping of records the hospital had to keep anyhow; and as much as fifty cents a tablet for aspirin.

The community non-profit hospitals might charge $20 a day for a bed in a ward, and then charge the patient $50 for the use of the operating room. In order to attract patients, the proprietary hospitals would cut their charge for a ward bed from $20 to $16 a day, or even to $12 a day, and then hike their charge for the operating room to $80 or $100, just as the supermarket cuts the price of hamburger and raises that of mayonnaise the same day.

Some proprietors began to make exorbitant profits, and some patients began to complain.

The situation became so serious in the summer of 1959 that the Hospital Council of Southern California took action to preserve or restore the reputations of hospitals. The Council drew up a set of principles which forced the hospitals of Southern California to provide a uniform system of rates, write bills that could be understood, establish fair charges for all services, show the charges in charts that patients could read, and establish a grievance procedure.

The grievance procedure was the most important part of the change. After 1960 the patient had somewhere to turn if he felt he had been cheated in the hospital. Not all of Southern California's hospitals would agree to this program, but about 150 of them did, and they began trying to rebuild their good name.

The Council became a clearing house for complaints, which began pouring in by the dozens, scores, and hundreds. In 1964, after four years of operation, the Council still received some 20 calls a week from people who felt they had been cheated on their hospital bills. Every call

was followed up. Sometimes it concerned a medical matter, and this was referred to the county medical association. If the complaint concerned a hospital matter, the
council asked that it be put in writing.

Once the written complaint was received, the Council
sent a letter to the administrator of the hospital, with a
copy to the grievance-committee member for the area in
which that hospital was located. The administrator of the
offending hospital was given first chance to reply. If he
could not satisfy the regional representative, then the education and grievance committee would take up the complaint.

The complaint would be brought before this committee,
and if the administrator could not explain it, he would be
warned. If it continued to offend, the hospital would be
withdrawn from the list of those that abide by what are
called "the guiding principles," and if the hospital was a
member of the Council, it would be ejected.

In 1964 some 200 complaints were reviewed by the
grievance committee, out of a total of 1,000 complaints.
The other 800 were settled before they came to the committee. Of those 200 complaints, three-quarters alleged
excessive charges, or charges for items or services not actually received. Others involved ethics and standards of
care.

Of the complaints, fifty-three percent were upheld by
the grievance committee. Seventy percent of these were
declared to be bookkeeping errors. And that came directly
to the point: in California and everywhere else the careful
hospital patient examined his hospital bill and demanded
that it be broken down for him into readable language.

Neither community hospitals nor proprietary hospitals
could be given a completely clean bill of health in the

matter of billings. All were prone to delivering to the patient a bill which had been drawn on an IBM or some other type of billing machine. The posting was done by clerks, who added the figures for each variety of charge and then put down the total. The patient, then, may see a figure for one day: for laboratory, $43.25. This might have represented six different laboratory tests, and in adding the six figures the billing clerk may have made a considerable error. Nor was it unknown for hospitals to charge, usually quite by mistake, for services the patient was never given.

For collecting, many hospitals used the billing-cycle technique, which meant that they printed a series of form letters, and sent these out one after the other at stipulated intervals until the bill was paid.

In Massachusetts, at Haverhill's Hale Hospital, city authorities in the summer of 1965 discovered a $700,000 backlog in unpaid bills which had been accumulating since 1952. The city manager suggested that a full-time credit manager be employed at this hospital, that the city take a "get tough" attitude towards hospital patients, use collection tactics, and take them to court if need be to collect. He suggested also that a person entering the hospital be required to make an advance payment or sign a bank note. Then, he said, Haverhill would be able to stop losing $50,000 to $60,000 a year on its hospital.

Hale Hospital would also arouse considerable community resentment by following such a program, and there, in a nutshell, was the hospital's fiscal dilemma in 1965.

Chapter Fifteen

THE FUTURE OF
THE AMERICAN HOSPITAL

Late in 1965 the Department of Defense announced that it was beginning to assemble data on hospitals in order to program all this material, feed it into a computer, and thus ascertain the components of the hospital of the future.

Until recent years the matter of hospital architecture had received very little attention. The development of new techniques in medical care (such as the intensive care plan), new services (such as intensive physiotherapy), and trends in the psychology of treatment (tending toward private rooms) brought challenges for architects which had not been fully realized. Until the 1960's few people ever bothered to worry about how well the design and construction of a hospital fit its functions. The late Frank Lloyd Wright used to worry about it. He never designed a hospital, but he talked about doing so many times. He had one fundamental principle of design for hospitals:

Sick people should never be allowed to see sick people,

226

he said. He quarreled with the multiple-floor building; the hospital should have one story, or two stories at most, he said. He thought there was need for decentralization of service, to get away from the institutional atmosphere that enwraps hospitals. He did not accept the need for a hospital like New York Hospital, with 35-story buildings; indeed, he did not accept the need for New York. He did concede that the hospital was the best-managed unit in American cities, but he said, nonetheless, that doctors and hospital administrators had not studied the psychology of the patient sufficiently:

"The psyche in which he (the sick man) finds himself should be attuned to health. In short, the emphasis in the new hospital should be on normality, not on the paraphernalia of abnormality. Death's head shows at once in the present hospital; grins there incessantly at any and every unfortunate victim. As a result, more people die of the hospital than of the illness they bring to it! Why is a hospital not as humane in practical, esthetic effect as it is humane in purpose?"

Frank Lloyd Wright had a vision. He called it Broadacre Hospital. It was to be low, rambling, and spacious, with homelike quarters. The surgery and therapeutic rooms would be hidden away in their places, like the plumbing and the heating systems in American houses of the twentieth century. Care of the sick would be the guiding factor in his hospital, not profit-making, nor management, nor the practice of medicine for the sake of scientific advance.

All services were to be free to the patient. Whether cost was to be paid by government or by philanthropy was a matter with which Wright did not concern himself. He was looking to the future of America, this much is certain.

Those in need of hospital service and the service itself must not be penalized by financial worries, Wright said.

What can the hospital be like in the future? Dr. Thomas Hale, the administrative vice-president of Albany Medical Center Hospital in New York State, asked that question of a number of hospital experts, and he received these replies:

—The transplanting of hearts, livers, and kidneys will become commonplace practice.

—Patients will go to sleep at night under electronic hypnosis.

—Food will be frozen in storage vaults, and prepared and served hot in minutes by the use of radiation heating. No more cold trays for anyone.

—Bed patients will all wear attachments that record respiration, pulse, and blood pressure at a central point.

—Television hook-ups will make it possible for specialists in far-off hospitals to be consulted on symptoms and problems. There will be far less moving around of consultants, and far fewer delays.

—Electronic computers will be used to diagnose disease, with an accuracy and speed far surpassing those of present methods. An accuracy of 95 percent is predicted.

—All pillows, sheets, and blankets, as well as food units, will be disposable.

In 1965, as those predictions were made, some were already being fulfilled in the advanced teaching hospitals. New York Hospital was pioneering in the attachment to record vital statistics on patients. The 1965 use was in acute cardiac cases, and the machinery was unwieldy but could be refined. Disposables were already common, although they had not reached the bedding level. Computers were in use in some hospitals.

Another indication of the future was to be found in the 710-bed Veterans Administration Hospital that opened in Washington in the spring of 1965. Every section of this hospital is fully automated, mechanically and electronically. A conveyor system carries supplies from central rooms in the basements to all four floors and all parts of the hospital. One system carries food trays mechanically to all four floors, another carries clean and soiled linens back and forth between the linen center and the floor storage rooms.

In the matter of hospital care, a most important development was the "automated hospital information system" which handled much of the paperwork formerly required of doctors and nurses. In 1965, a computer did the job.

The computer could do the paperwork of dozens of doctors and nurses. It compiled ward medication schedules, formerly a nurse's task which took many hours each day; it listed patient medication schedules. It kept drug inventories and noted needs for re-orders. It could take from the patient's medical history a drug sensitivity caution notice, without mistake, and be sure that the patient never had a drug that was wrong for him.

It controlled the patient's admission, medication, laboratory work, radiology, diet, surgery, and clinic treatment. All this information was checked and cross-checked. The computer even kept track of the personal funds the patient might have deposited with the hospital. The system could be used to take care of the patient after he was discharged, calling to the attention of the staff need for check-ups, medication, or follow-up care.

One of the most remarkable achievements of the computer was in making long-distance diagnosis of heart disease. The first test came when electrocardiograms from the VA hospital in West Roxbury, Massachusetts, were transmitted by telephone to a Washington computer, and after a six-second calculation the diagnosis was flashed back to the West Roxbury hospital by voice. The entire process, from beginning to end, took less than ten minutes. Thus, in the new hospital in Washington, difficult diagnoses could be and were made daily by this computer for VA hospitals all over the United States.

Physically, the small hospital of the future may be something like the 100-bed Community Hospital of Monterey Peninsula, sometimes called "the Carmel Hilton" by its patients. This is an architect's hospital, with overtones of the thinking of Frank Lloyd Wright. It was designed by Edward Durrell Stone with the needs of the patient in mind.

This hospital was built on the edge of Pebble Beach. The rooms were arranged on two floors, with views of the ocean or of the woods behind, or of both. It had nothing but private rooms, and it was built to have an intimacy that was almost unduplicated among hospitals of the 1960's. Everyone, from the architect to the physicians, wanted to avoid the institutional look.

The hospital sprawled around a central court, complete with fountain. It was non-functional, but the administrator of this hospital was proud of it because it set the tone the hospital wanted: tranquillity.

Opposite this court, in one wing, were located the four operating rooms, the recovery room, an X-ray suite, the intensive care department, the physical therapy unit, the emergency room, and the central supply room. On the other side were placed the administrative offices, the records rooms, the maternity unit, the laboratory, the kitchen, and a conference room. All this was well away from the

patients' rooms, following the Wright concept of keeping
the patient unaware of sickness and death as much as possible. Another development was the placement of a small
room near the surgery where families could go to wait in
private during critical hours, and where the surgeon could
talk to them without disturbing them or others.

With all its modern features, this hospital still turned
out to be cheaper to operate than the old variety. Room
rates for private rooms there cost just about what semi-
private rooms cost in other California hospitals, $27-$31
per day. Nursing hours dropped from 5.1 per patient per
day in the old community hospital to 4.7.

The private room for patients was surely coming as the
standard facility, just as the private nurse was going to be
replaced by the intensive care unit. In Lincoln, Nebraska,
the Lincoln General Hospital proposed to build a 120-bed
addition, all private rooms. Genesee Hospital, in Rochester, New York, also developed small, low-cost rooms. The
great problem to overcome was the bureaucracy of Blue
Cross, which focused on the semi-private room, and has
stuck with that concept in the face of the changing mores
of medicine.

Doctors discovered in the 1960's that the semi-private
room was a factor in delaying recovery of some patients.
The curtains that separated beds are no substitute for privacy. They did not muffle snoring, moaning, coughing, or
talk. A cluster of visitors to one patient might disturb the
other patient. The non-smoker might be afflicted with a
heavy-smoking roommate.

Psychiatrists said that shared accommodations might
even bring about psychiatric complications that delay recovery.

So the trend in hospitals was, on the one hand, for more

patient comfort; on the other was the lessening of the personal relationship between the patient and the hospital as those in charge concentrated more on science and the fight against disease, and less on the individuality of the patient.

In the future there can be better hospitals, and closer supervision of standards; there probably will be fewer rural hospitals because such substandard institutions will fall by the wayside. There will be more doctors and more nurses, but the patient will see less of them. Care in the general hospitals will become more impersonal, although more scientific and accurate in the details of fighting disease. The general hospital will not even be a general hospital any more, but an "acute" hospital, where the patient will go during the severe stages of his disease or injury. He will be attended to quickly, and moved out quickly into a unit that specializes in care. Here he will receive the attention he has been longing for, not from nurses of the new school, but from practical nurses, social workers, and aides who will perform the functions so long associated with nursing. Sooner than he thinks, he will be sent home, where he will be called upon by doctors, nurses, therapists, and other specialists of the health world. Then he will be on his own, and his health activity will be in the charge of an electronic computer which will keep the hospital authorities aware of his existence, and call him to the attention of forgetful human beings at the proper times.

The major hospital problem in America in 1965 was that not enough Americans were receiving the best hospital care that some few Americans were receiving, and the difference was not based on ability to pay but on the luck or ability to find one's way into a good hospital where the best of care was obtainable.

The problem would continue until America had evened out its hospital program, until the promised complexes of regional hospitals spread like a network across the country, until the farmer in North Dakota and the sharecropper in Alabama could receive the same care as the student at Yale University.

In terms of care within the hospital, we may be coming toward a system that has long been practiced in other parts of the world, with variations. In 1965, Dr. Edwin F. Rosinski and Dr. Frederick J. Spencer of the Medical College of Virginia published the results of their investigations into the use of assistant medical officers in the Fiji Islands, Papua, Tanganyika, Kenya, and Ethiopia. U.S. government health officials began talking about the possible use of "assistant doctors" who would be more highly trained than registered nurses, and might be extremely valuable in rural areas.[1]

The USSR has been using such a program for a number of years. In 1960 there were 401,612 doctors in the USSR, plus 334,700 *feldshers*, or assistant medical officers. In Iran, doctors are trained for seven years, while *behdars*, or assistants, are trained for four years, and perform some of the functions, in hospitals and out of them, that doctors formerly performed.

All of these ideas represented important developments, yet they did not attack frontally the two major problems of American hospitalization that existed in 1966: the provision of a higher standard of hospital care for the majority of Americans, and the provision of the best care for all Americans at rates that were equitable and allowed hospi-

234 Condition Critical

tals to operate without the burden of constant deficit or the need for ever-rising rates to meet ever-rising costs.

There were lessons to be learned on the North American continent, from Canada, whose medical and hospital systems were more like those of the United States than of any other nation. Canadian and American hospitals both belonged to the American Hospital Association, the administrators of both read the same publications, and they compared notes about common problems.

In 1960, in Canada, there were 1,372 hospitals of all kinds (public, private and federal government). They provided 190,000 beds for Canadians, or 10.6 beds per 1,000 population—a figure significantly higher than the 9.1 beds per thousand of the United States. The doctor population of Canada was not quite as high as that of the United States, in relation to the population (1/900 as compared to the U.S. 1/710). Socially, in 1965, Canada moved toward even more complete hospital care for its citizens, with the pledge of Prime Minister Lester Pearson that Medicare, or national health insurance, would be available to every Canadian citizen. The Canadian program had not come without a struggle.

The struggle began in 1962 with a battle between the doctors and the government of Saskatchewan, when that province inaugurated a government health service. A year later Alberta put its own Medicare program into effect. Later Newfoundland began a limited hospital program, and Ontario did the same. At the end of 1965, following a narrow victory in a national election, Prime Minister Pearson moved ahead with the Liberal Party's program to bring government-backed medical care to all of Canada. The plan would provide every Canadian with medical services. Every child would receive dental services up to the age of 18. All Canadians would be eligible for mental-health care. Free drugs would be supplied to patients.

There was much conflict about the manner in which total medical care would be brought to Canada, but very little conflict about the need for it, or its inevitability. The arguments were tied up with the rights of provinces versus those of the federal government, and the struggle of Quebec to retain her French individuality. "Eventually, one way or another," said Premier John Robarts of Ontario, "we'll achieve Medicare for the people from coast to coast. As a question of social development, it's inevitable. It's a matter of how we get there."

The Pearson plan called for the Canadian federal government to pay half the cost of Medicare, perhaps $500,-000,000 a year. The ten provinces would administer the health services and pay the other half of the cost. The benefits would cover all services of physicians and would apply to all citizens, regardless of ability to pay. The plans would be publicly administered, and they must be flexible enough and uniform enough that a citizen of any province could move to another province and retain his benefits. Also, if a citizen of one province fell ill while visiting in another province, he would be assured of his benefits.

Ontario's hospital-insurance plan covered ninety-eight percent of the people of the province. Participation was mandatory for all, except the self-employed and those who worked in firms with fewer than 15 employees. Even these could be covered if they chose to be voluntary subscribers, and most of them did.

The Ontario Hospital Insurance Plan offered coverage for what the Canadians call "essential hospital care." It did not cover medical or surgical fees. It was open to every resident of the province. The cost to an individual subscriber was about $25 a year, or about $50 a year to a family. (This compared with a limited Blue Cross policy in New York State for a family, which in 1965 cost $216 a year.)

Under the Ontario plan the patient may enter any general hospital, convalescent hospital, chronic disease hospital, tuberculosis sanatorium, or provincial mental hospital. Some proprietary hospitals had been approved for the plan, but not many.

Even if the patient fell ill outside Ontario the benefits would be paid, but only such benefits as would be paid in Ontario.

What services were available? These:

—room and meals at the ward level.
—nursing, when provided by the hospital.
—laboratory, radiological, and diagnostic procedures, plus treatment or disease-prevention procedures.
—drugs, and biologicals prescribed by doctors.
—use of operating room and other hospital facilities.
—routine surgical supplies.
—radiotherapy facilities.
—physiotherapy facilities.
—any services rendered by persons who were paid by the hospital.

The plan also covered emergency outpatient treatment for fractures and other injuries or diseases.

It did not provide for semi-private rooms or private rooms. Diagnostic treatment was not included in the benefits, nor were nursing or medical fees, surgical fees, home care, or ambulance or any other transportation.

The federal plan was to increase these services, make them available nationally, and supplement them with

medical and surgical services for which the people would
pay fixed insurance fees.

In the United States, with the twin concerns of high
cost to the patient and inadequate hospital facilities for
the nation at large, the problem was how the necessary
progress could be made, and quickly, in raising the standards of hospital care. Increasing the number of hospital
beds per thousand population, and cutting the cost to the
individual patient, were matters that must be faced on
the government level. It could be said in 1966 that the
better hospitals had done virtually everything possible to
solve their own financial problems, and still those problems persisted and increased.[2]

Dr. Ray E. Trussell, former New York City hospital
commissioner and head of Columbia University's School
of Public Health, said that the major concern of responsible leaders in the medical care field was that Medicare
might bring a limit on the drive to elevate health standards, including hospital standards.[3]

Toward the end of 1965, after fifteen new laws affecting
American health care had been passed by Congress, a
White House Conference was called to attempt to settle
some of the outstanding issues dividing hospitals, medical
men, and government in the health field.[4] John W. Gardner, Secretary of Health, Education and Welfare, suggested a real partnership of government with hospitals
and the various groups of organized medicine.

Earlier, in accepting the Distinguished Service Award
of the American Hospital Association, Dr. Albert W.
Snoke, director of Yale-New Haven Hospital, and a past
president of the AHA, issued a warning to hospital men
and doctors for the future:

"I have become increasingly aware of the importance

of that amorphous group labeled "The Public"—whether made up of patients, board members, representatives of Congress, or organized non-medical groups—in the development of our present ways of caring for health and disease. The growth in knowledge and in sophistication in health affairs on the part of these non-professional partners is only natural and proper. If we, the hospitals and the physicians, are to be honest and realistic, we must recognize that the public and its representatives, through politics, social and economic organizations, must and will have a final voice in our policies and our activities. They are presently looking to us for guidance. If we don't respond, they must make their decisions without us. It is up to us to give them facts to assist in their judgments."

Dr. C. C. Cutting, executive director of the Permanente Medical Group of Oakland, California, forecast the development of all health care into three major divisions of medicine.[5] These would be, he said, Health Care, which would be preventive medicine; Predictive Care, which would be the discovery of symptoms early to prevent serious illness; and Sickness Care, which might involve far more transplants of organs and use of artificial organs than anyone in 1965 could imagine.

All these programs, and all planning, must be placed in the hands of physicians and not lay persons, Dr. Cutting said. In a way, then, he was suggesting the incorporation of hospital administration, in 1965 a lay specialty, as a medical specialty.

Having fought Medicare down to the wire, and lost, having fought the regional medical center program down to the wire, and lost, the American Medical Association's House of Delegates finally agreed, reluctantly, to cooperate with the government. At its December, 1965, meeting, this body appointed 45 representatives to the six technical committees that would handle Medicare regulations, and these advisors began work with the government. There was much hemming and hawing. The major fear of the physicians was that government might move in to control the doctors' fees, and it was apparent as Medicare began that there would be many thorny problems ahead in the improvement of the American health system, since it was being improved at the behest of what Dr. Snoke termed the medical men's "non-professional partners."

Even before the machinery of Medicare was established, certain trends had become apparent to experts in the field. One, mentioned by Dr. Trussell, was that Medicare was almost certain to take the pressure off public hospitals, in 1966 overburdened with charity patients, many of them elderly. The old people, their bills guaranteed by government, would become desirable patients to private hospitals, and this would tend to free public hospitals, many of which were teaching hospitals, from floods of those suffering from diseases of old age.

The coming change would be even more far-reaching. Voluntary hospitals would be relieved of the pressure of supporting many patients who could not pay, although not relieved of all those problems. Americans were accepting the general world principle that public health was a public responsibility, and that it began at the personal health level.

The great change that had come to the United States with the passage of Medicare was overlooked by many, but it was stated succinctly by Secretary Gardner after the White House Conference. He talked of creating whole systems in the health field, based on cooperation by state, federal, and local governments with those directly concerned in American health, both in and out of hospitals.

Medicare had created a new system, a new responsibility for the health of a segment of the American public by federal authorities. No other agency in the United States had proved willing or able to undertake the task, although the matter had been under discussion for more than 30 years.

Until Medicare was passed, some 40,000,000 people in the United States were not covered by any form of health insurance at a time when hospital and medical costs were rising at so rapid a rate that health insurance had become a necessity. Medicare brought health insurance to more than 19,000,000 people, those over 65 years of age, but many of these already had some form of health insurance. Perhaps 25,000,000 to 30,000,000 Americans were still not covered by any form of health insurance even after the passage of Medicare. The trend in social legislation indicated that they would not remain unprotected for very long.

In passing the Medicare law, Congress had made it clear that the burden for American health care in 1965 did not rest only on voluntary programs or state or local programs, but that the federal authority was accepting that burden. This would mean closer federal examination of hospital standards, and the pressure would be on the Joint Commission on Hospital Accreditation to improve the standards that many experts in the field of public health said were too low. The pressure would be on the states to improve and enforce their standards, and on local governments and voluntary and private hospitals to improve theirs.

Never in the history of the United States had so much attention been given to the problems of public health by so many diverse elements in American society. It seemed possible at the beginning of 1966 that the United States could assume a position of leadership in public health, for the public was aroused and would brook no interference or retreat. But the United States was still numbered fifteenth among the nations of the world in the provision of hospital facilities for its people, and the best in hospital care was still not available to every American, whether for reasons of geography, race, economic status, or hospital backwardness. Only when those statements could no longer be made would the United States have solved its pressing hospital problems.

HOSPITAL
CHECK LIST

Before you enter a hospital, if you have any choice, follow this check list for your own protection. It will assure you of the best care you can receive in an American hospital.

1. Your physician or surgeon is a member of the hospital staff.

2. Your physician or surgeon holds a diploma from an American Specialty Board, is a fellow of an American college, or has a staff appointment at a voluntary or municipal hospital.

3. Your hospital or nursing home is accredited by the Joint Commission established by the American Medical Association, American Hospital Association, American College of Physicians, and American College of Surgeons.

4. If you are undergoing surgery, an anesthesiologist, a medical doctor, will preside over the administration of your anesthesia.

5. Before the operation you will have a pre-anesthetic

examination to determine any physical weaknesses that might affect the operation, or the use of anesthesia.

6. The hospital has the services of a pathologist, who examines tissues removed in an operation promptly, and makes prompt report to the surgeon.

7. The hospital maintains a recovery room into which you will be placed after the operation, with constant supervision.

8. Your doctor and anesthesiologist remain with you after the operation until you are sensitive to pain.

9. The hospital maintains simple heart aids such as defibrillators, in case your heart action stops or goes out of control temporarily.

10. The hospital has an intensive care section into which you may be placed if you need constant surveillance.

11. The hospital has the services of a radiologist, who reads and interprets all X-rays within 24 hours after they are taken.

12. The hospital has the services of a graduate pharmacist, who supervises the packaging and dosages of all drugs.

13. The hospital administration will present you with an itemized bill on request, from which you can check every charge for drugs, laboratory tests, X-rays and special services.

ACKNOWLEDGMENTS

The author owes his first debt of thanks to Robert Loomis of Random House, who suggested this idea and offered some valuable information. He is also indebted to Stephen Gamble and a number of officials of the Southern California Hospital Council for information, to nurses at Hollywood's Presbyterian Hospital, and to several private nurses in Los Angeles. A number of physicians gave important information but very few of them wanted to be mentioned by name, except those, below, who were connected with hospitals in one way or another, other than as members of the medical staff.

Emalie Mader of the Los Angeles County General Hospital was very helpful, as were other employees and nurses in that hospital. Arthur L. Cook, assistant business manager of the Dallas Medical and Surgical Clinic and Hospital was helpful. So were officials of Parkland and Dallas Methodist Hospitals, and several Dallas doctors.

F. R. Hood, director of information for the Veterans Administration, provided valuable information. So did Dr. Dawson Tyson, chief of staff of the VA hospital at White River Junction, Vermont, and John O'Connell, administrative assistant to the chief of staff. A number of people at the Mary Hitchcock Memorial Hospital and clinic were helpful, from the public relations department, to the

244

administrative office. The author is especially grateful to Dorothea Bartlett, chief dietician of Mary Hitchcock Memorial.

Francis C. Houghton, administrator of Rutland Hospital, gave the author a considerable amount of valuable time. Dr. James A. Reedy of Fair Haven was helpful. So were Mrs. Bernard R. McCann and Robert Juckett, nursing-home proprietors in Castleton and Fair Haven, Vermont.

Dr. Ray Trussell of the Columbia University School of Public Health and Administrative Medicine was very helpful. So was Dr. Henry N. Pratt, director of New York Hospital. David W. Walsh, vice-president of Memorial Hospital, was kind enough to submit to an interview. Several nurses and public relations girls in the hospital gave the author information, too. In New York City the author is indebted to a number of doctors, and especially to C. F., who supplied a considerable amount of accurate information about doctors' problems and the problem of doctors in that city.

In New Haven, Dr. Albert Snoke, director of Yale-New Haven Hospital, went far out of his way to be helpful. So did Al Friedge of the hospital public relations staff. In Hartford, Dr. A. W. Partington spent a considerable amount of time showing the author the emergency room and explaining its functions at that hospital.

Other hospitals and administrators who helped the author include: Herbert Anderson, director of the Connecticut Hospital Association, New Haven; several persons at the Connecticut Nurses' Association, H. J. Semingson, Trinity Hospital, Minot, North Dakota; Hilo Hospital, Hilo, Hawaii; The Reading Hospital, Reading, Pennsylania; Providence Hospital, Mobile, Alabama; St. Gabriel's Hospital, Little Falls, Montana; Ketchikan Hospital, Ketchikan, Alaska; Vancouver Memorial Hospital, Vancouver, Washington; Donald L. Ford, South County Hospital, Wakefield, Rhode Island; E. H. White, Administrator, Valley Hospital, Tremonton, Utah; Boehne Hospital, Evansville, Indiana; Mercy Hospital, Devils Lake, North Dakota; Brattleboro Retreat, Brattleboro, Vermont; Dr. Henry A. Davidson, Superintendent, County Overbrook Hospital, Cedar Grove, New Jersey; Gilmore Memorial Hospital, Armory, Mississippi; Robert E. Holtzer, Memorial Hospital, Abilene, Kansas; Booth Memorial Hospital, The Salvation Army, Boise, Idaho; The Espanola Hospital, Espanola, New Mexico; Beth Israel Hospital,

Boston; Kent General Hospital, Dover, Delaware; Austin S. Hall, Administrator, Beverly Hills Doctors Hospital, Beverly Hills, California; Bowling Green Hospital, Warren County, Kentucky; Kings Daughters Hospital, Frankfort, Kentucky; Helena Hospital, Helena, Arkansas; Herbert J. Thomas Memorial Hospital, South Charleston, West Virginia; Harry C. Wheeler, Deaconess Hospital, Spokane, Washington; Sitka Community Hospital, Sitka, Alaska; St. Joseph's Hospital, Breese, Illinois; Alice Peck Day Memorial Hospital, Lebanon, New Hampshire; Pioneer Memorial Hospital, Prineville, Oregon; Sister Mary Alexine, Administrator, St. John's Hospital, Helena, Montana; W. B. Sheldon, Margaretville Hospital, Margaretville, New York; Fergus Falls Hospital, Fergus Falls, Minnesota; Perkins County Community Hospital, Grant, Nebraska; A. Chesley Wilson, Jr., Director of Public Information, The American Hospital Association; Memorial Hospital, Gulfport, Mississippi; Dr. Leigh J. Grozier, Director, Hermann Hospital, Houston, Texas; Washoe Medical Center, Reno, Nevada; Community Hospital, Battle Creek, Michigan; St. Francis Hospital, Topeka, Kansas; Baptist Hospital, Miami, Florida; Ponca City Hospital, Ponca City, Oklahoma; St. Olaf Hospital, Austin, Minnesota; St. Mary's Hospital, Pierre, South Dakota; Community Hospital, Anderson, Indiana; plus some fifty other hospitals whose administrators preferred to remain anonymous.

Albert J. O'Brien, executive director of Lawrence Hospital in Bronxville, New York, was helpful in discussing the strike of some hospital employees there in the spring of 1965. Leon Davis, President of Local 1199, Drug and Hospital Employees Union, was also helpful, as was Moe Foner, executive secretary of the Union. Marie Schirmer of the Greater New York Hospital Fund steered the author to several sources of information. Jan Tyroler of Mt. Sinai Hospital in New York City was very helpful.

William J. Stout, administrator of the Cyril and Julia C. Johnson Memorial Hospital in Stafford Springs, Connecticut, was kind enough to talk to the author extensively about hospital problems in general. Paul Sternlof, administrator of Sharon Hospital, in Sharon, Connecticut, gave all the time the author asked, and read portions of the manuscript for accuracy.

The controller of Sharon Hospital was most helpful, as were

clerks, secretaries, nurses, laboratory technicians, and many others at that hospital. Edward Heacox, pharmacist, explained the Brewer system and several other technical aspects of the hospital's pharmacy operation.

The author is most grateful to A. Chesley Wilson, Jr., director of public information for the American Hospital Association, Millard E. Krebs, assistant director, and to Bruce R. Sanderson, assistant director of the Joint Commission on Accreditation of Hospitals, for information about the Hospital Association's activities, the Joint Commission, and hospital problems in general.

Julie Kerry, chief nurse at New Milford Hospital showed the author how drugs are dispensed in a small hospital, and discussed nursing problems.

Edward S. Baron, administrator of New Milford Hospital, New Milford, Connecticut, told the author about the unfortunate accident in his hospital, and contributed considerable information about hospitals in the state. Peter Bucky of the Bucky X-ray International Company told the author details about hospitals and about the expense of some hospital equipment.

The author owes a considerable debt to William H. White, executive editor of *Medical World News*, who gave the author several magazine assignments in the health field in 1962, and in a way created the interest that led to this book. His excellent publication was consulted steadily for three years in the preparation of the book.

Dr. Alfred Rizzolo of the Harlem Valley State Hospital in Wingdale, New York, was most gracious with his time and instructed the author in the ways of the New York State Department of Mental Hygiene as well as the particular problems of his hospital and the patients who come there.

Dr. Carl C. Gruhzit, head of the pharmacology department at Hong Kong University, discussed several aspects of the medical-economic picture with the author, including hospital techniques in the British Commonwealth.

At the Mary Hitchcock Memorial Hospital in Hanover, New Hampshire, John K. Springer, associate administrator, was of great assistance. Robert T. Ross, information services director, and his staff provided the author with much material about their hospital and others. Miss Dorothea Bartlett, head of the department of dietetics discussed the hospital's food planning and service departments.

Ladislas Farago shared with the author the tale of his tribulations with hospitals over the years, and this was basic to the book.

The author is also very much indebted to Eli C. Minton of Dallas, for much chauffeuring around that city, for information leads, and for research work in the Dallas health field.

Olga G. Hoyt assisted with the research and the editing of the manuscript.

A considerable volume of documents, bulletins, pamphlets, and institutional publications was consulted during the research for this book. They include the statement of policy of the Bureau of Public Assistance of Los Angeles County, California; the County Hospitals Basic Information Reference for that county; the Los Angeles County Hospital publication *In General*; *Standards for Hospital Accreditation of the Joint Commission on Accreditation of Hospitals*; *Standards for Extended Care of the Joint Commission on Accreditation of Hospitals*; Residency Training Program in Anesthesiology, Memorial Hospital; Training programs in Pediatrics, same; Residency Training Programs in X-ray Diagnosis, same; *Intramural Clinical Research Bulletin*, same; *Bulletin of the Memorial School for X-ray Technicians;* Memorial Hospital's Bulletin *Information for Patients.*

The author also consulted the following: *The Quantity, Quality, and Costs of Medical and Hospital Care Secured by a Sample of Teamster Families in the New York Area,* a survey conducted under the auspices of the Columbia University School of Public Health and Administrative Medicine, 1964; *The Report of the New York State Advisory Committee,* made at the request of the U.S. Commission on Civil Rights, 1963; *New York Hospital News; Questions and Answers on Health Insurance of the Aged,* Department of Health, Education and Welfare, Social Security Administration, 1965; *The Record* of New York Hospital; *The Annual Report of the Society of the New York Hospital,* 1964; the third report, 1962-63 of Memorial Sloan-Kettering Cancer Center; *Evaluation of Nursing Homes,* Vermont State Health Department, 1962; *Hospitalization for Mental Illness in New York State,* published by the Department of Mental Hygiene, 1965; Charge Cards of the New York Hospital; Running financial account of New Milford Hospital, New Milford, Connecticut, through September, 1964; 1964 *Annual Report of Mary Hitchcock Memorial Hospital,* Hanover, New Hampshire; *Hospital News,* publication of Local 1199, Hospital and Drug Workers Union; *Progress Report, Guiding Principles for Hospitals as Developed by the Hospital Council of Southern California;* Special Report of Grace-New Haven Community Hospital to Dr. Albert Snoke on Patient Refunds as Result of Two Insurances, November, 1964; *Voluntary Health Insurance in the United States as of December 31, 1965,* published by the Health Insurance Council; *Ontario Hospital Insurance,* Ontario Hospital Services Commission; *Annual Report Grace-New Haven Community Hospital,* 1964; *Annual Report, Rutland Hospital,* 1964.

A number of books were consulted but the most valuable of these in terms of the patient was *Hospitals, Doctors, and Dollars,* by Robert M. Cunningham, Jr., published by F. W. Dodge Corporation in New York in 1960. This is largely a collection of Mr. Cunningham's writing as editor of *The Modern Hospital.* Other books were consulted on special hospital problems such as economics, and care, including *The Give and Take in Hospitals* by Burling, Lentz and Wilson, G. P. Putnam's Sons, 1956. The problem of using books in discussing the hospital crisis of the 1960's is that times were changing so rapidly that the solid, scholarly studies of hospitals were moving rapidly out of date.

John Starr's *Hospital City,* Crown, New York, 1957, and Joseph Hirsh and Beka Doherty's *Mount Sinai Hospital of New York, the First 100 Years,* were valuable as pictures of life in the big hospitals. The author also used his own *Short History of Science,* John Day, for general information and the history of hospitals. Most of the research for this book was prepared through magazine, newspaper, technical journal, interview, and a private survey sent to some 300 American hospitals in the fifty states of the Union by the author. Some hospitals did not reply at all. Some replied answering only part of the questionnaire. About half wished to remain anonymous, and the remainder were willing to cooperate openly. The author is most grateful to them.

Elizabeth Edwards, director of the Chattanooga, Tennessee, library system, went to a great deal of extra trouble to secure information for the author, and in conversation gave several leads for important ideas to be considered in this study. The author owes her a special debt of thanks.

Publications consulted in this study include: *Medical World News, Hospitals, The Modern Hospital, Hospital Forum, Medical Economics, U.S. News and World Report, Time, Newsweek,* and *Harper's.*

Newspapers consulted include the New York *Times,* the New York *Herald Tribune,* the New York *Post,* the New York *Journal-American,* the New York *World-Telegram and Sun,* the Denver *Post,* the Los Angeles *Times,* the Tucson *Star,* the El Paso *Post and Herald,* the Dallas *Morning News,* the Shreveport *Times,* the Birmingham *News,* the Chattanooga *Times,* the La Puente Valley (California) *Herald,* the Waterbury *Republican,* the New Haven *Register,* the Hartford *Courant,* the Rutland *Herald,* the Boston *Globe,* the Boston *Advertiser.*

NOTES

Chapter One

1 U.S., 9.1 per thousand; Canada, 10.6; Sweden, 15.6; Switzerland, 13.6; United Kingdom, 10.1 (plus 101 non-national health service hospitals); Norway, 10.2; Luxembourg, 11.1; Ireland, 15.2; Iceland, 10.3; Federal Republic of Germany, 10.7; France, 11.0; Finland, 9.2; Denmark, 10.4; Austria, 10.6; New Zealand, 11.0.

   Actually the American position was even worse in the 1960's than it appeared to be on the surface. In 1948, when there were 6,335 registered hospitals in the United States, the average was 9.8 beds per thousand population. In the next two decades, hospital construction was so badly neglected that the relative position worsened radically.

2 U.S., 9.4 deaths per thousand population; Canada, 7.8; USSR, 7.1; Norway, 9.0; Iceland, 7.2; Finland, 8.9; Denmark, 9.3; Greece, 7.4; Netherlands, 7.6.

3 U.S., 26.4 deaths per thousand babies born; Sweden, 16.6; Switzerland, 21.1; United Kingdom (England and Wales only) 21.8; Norway, 18.7; Iceland, 16.4; France, 23.3; Finland, 21.0; Denmark, 22.5; The Netherlands, 16.5.

4 By 1948, nearly all hospitals in the world except those in North America were government operated, and most countries in the world were moving toward total national or government health programs. The United States government hospital programs began with the Hill-Burton hospital construction program in the 1940's, under which nearly $4 billion was given to hospitals to modernize and expand, on a matching fund basis; the Kerr-Mills bill of 1960, under which the federal government contributed from 50 to 80 percent of the cost of hospital care for the old poor. None of these was satisfactory. The United States moved steadily backward, relatively, in construction of

251

hospitals and hospital beds. At the end of two years only 30 states had accepted the conditions of Kerr-Mills matching funds, and these state-administered programs varied so widely that it could not be said there *was* a single program.

5 Compare personnel and expense figures with 1948, for example.

	1948	1965
Number of hospitals	6,335	7,127
Number of beds	1,423,520	1,696,039
Number of personnel	939,000	1,886,839
Payroll	$1,163,300,000	$7,974,623,000

6 Also, there was serious misconception in America about the size of hospital endowments. In 1948, American Hospital Association figures showed the average endowment of non-government, non-profit American hospitals was about $100,000 per hospital. Then, and in 1965, 90% of all hospital costs were met by charges to patients or insurance payers.

7 The Journal of the American Medical Association, December 20, 1965.

8 Report of Joint Commission on Accreditation of Hospitals, 1965.

9 World Health Organization, *Second Report on the World Health Situation 1957-1960*, Geneva, January, 1963.

10 The Moslem world was several hundred years ahead of the West in medicine and hospitalization. Before Salerno, Arab hospitals existed at Baghdad in the Eastern Moslem world, and in Egypt and Spain. Much of the West's early medical and hospital knowledge was transmitted from Spain to Italy, sometimes by way of Sicily.

11 Eventually this hospital became Philadelphia General Hospital.

12 In each ambulance a box beneath the driver's seat contained a quart flask of brandy, two tourniquets, half a dozen bandages, half a dozen small sponges, splint material, pieces of blanket for padding, strips of various lengths of cloths with buckles for compresses, and a two ounce vial of persulphate of iron. Altogether it was a far more impressive display of concern for the emergency patient than New York hospitals would display a century later, when many did not carry accepted emergency supplies, such as resuscitators and bottles of oxygen.

13 For the times this was most advanced. The ratio of hospital beds to population in the U.S. was then 1.9 per thousand, or about that of Nicaragua in 1963.

14 These same tendencies developed in Europe, but far more fully and decisively. By 1948 nearly all the world's hospitals were under government control. A few small hospitals (usually less than 50 beds) were maintained by private physicians for treatment of the wealthy,

but these comprised only five percent of the total bed capacity of the world by that year.

15 Average time for hospitalization for tuberculosis was three years.

16 In 1965, 7,127 hospitals were registered by the American Hospital Association, but only 4,204 were accredited by the Joint Commission on Accreditation of Hospitals. These accredited hospitals accounted for 86.3 percent of all patient admissions.

17 The study is part of a continuing study made on behalf of the Teamsters Joint Council No. 16 in New York City to provide the Union's membership with continuing studies of the scope and quality of medical services used by the membership under the forms of health and hospital insurance available to the Teamsters and their families. During the year 1962, a total of 6,679 members of the Teamsters Union and their families were admitted to hospitals in New York City. Of these, 375 admissions were taken for study. Among the conclusions of the surveyors: "Projection of the study findings indicated that if all the New York City admissions in 1962 had been reviewed, the problem of 'less than optimal' medical care would have occurred in between 39 and 51 percent of the admissions and the problem of questionable admissions in between 12 and 20 percent of the admissions."

Chapter Two

1 Breakdown of percentage of occupancy in 1964 by categories: Pavilion (ward): medical, 87.2%; Surgical, 92.5%; Urological, 82.5%; Obstetrical and gynecological, 58.5%; Pediatrics, 68.1%; Private rooms: Main hospital, 94.1%; Obstetrical and gynecological, 87.4%; Pediatrics, 92.3%; Semi-private rooms: Two-bed rooms, Baker Pavilion, 92.9%; Main Hospital, 81.1%; Obstetrical and gynecological, 85.8%; Pediatrics, 81.4%.

2 New York Hospital's annual report for 1964 showed the following breakdown, interesting because it also gave a quick picture of the rise in costs in one short year and the drastic raise in charges:

Patient Services	1964	1963
Average cost per patient day	$63.22	$58.30
Average income per patient day	59.59	51.40
Average loss per patient day	3.63	6.90
Out-patients		
Average cost per patient visit	$11.72	$12.45
Average income per patient visit	4.71	4.72
Average loss per patient visit	7.01	7.73

3 American Hospital Association figures for 1964: California, 138,722 beds; New York, 227,528 beds.

Chapter Three

1 American Hospital Association figures for 1963: Federal, 446; State, 561; County, 826; City, 345; City-County, 75; Hospital District, 200.
2 In 1963 when all American hospital beds totalled 1,701,839, state and local government psychiatric beds in 328 hospitals totalled 693,827. The federal government operated 67,000 psychiatric beds. Non-government hospitals accounted for fewer than 21,000 beds in that field.
3 Canadian hospitals in provinces where government hospital insurance is in effect have experienced longer patient stays with the coming of insurance, and this is attributed to reduction of economic pressure on the patient.

Chapter Four

1 In 1946 American Hospital Association figures showed there were 1,076 short-term proprietary hospitals in the United States, containing 39,000 beds, and admitting 1,408,000 patients annually. In 1963 there were only 896 proprietary hospitals, but they contained 44,000 beds and admitted 1,832,000 patients. Altogether in 1963, including long term hospitals, there were 1,022 proprietary hospitals in the United States.
2 The regions are: New England: Connecticut, Maine, New Hampshire, Vermont, Rhode Island, Massachusetts; Middle Atlantic: Pennsylvania, New Jersey, New York; South Atlantic: Delaware, District of Columbia, Florida, Georgia, Maryland, North Carolina, South Carolina, Virginia, West Virginia; East North Central: Illinois, Indiana, Michigan, Ohio, Wisconsin; East South Central: Alabama, Kentucky, Mississippi, Tennessee; West North Central: Iowa, Kansas, Minnesota, Missouri, Nebraska, North Dakota, South Dakota; West South Central: Arkansas, Louisiana, Oklahoma, Texas; Mountain: Arizona, Colorado, Idaho, Montana, Nevada, New Mexico, Utah, Wyoming; Pacific: Alaska, California, Hawaii, Oregon, Washington.
3 This figure includes Alabama with 33 proprietary hospitals; Kentucky, 33; Mississippi, 7; Missouri, 13; Tennessee, 45; Arkansas, 18; Louisiana, 61; Texas, 215; Florida, 21; Georgia, 19; North Carolina, 13; South Carolina, 6; Virginia, 25; West Virginia, 26. It does not include the District of Columbia or Oklahoma.

	Number	Percent of admissions	Cost per patient day
4 Nonfederal short-term general and other special	5,712	94.3	$41.58
Voluntary nonprofit	3,402	65.9	42.47
Proprietary	870	6.5	43.01
State and local government	1,440	19.5	38.57
Nonfederal long-term	300	0.6	18.91
Federal	441	5.7	27.17

Chapter Six

1 Dr. James Appel, President of the American Medical Association said in the fall of 1965 that the United States will need 550,000 doctors by the end of the century. In 1965 there were 282,844 licensed physicians in practice. A special commission of the U.S. Surgeon General's office estimated that year that 330,000 physicians would be required by 1975, and that to bring the number of doctors up, 20 new medical schools must be built in the coming decade, at an estimated cost of $6,100,000,000.

2 Residency scales vary in various cities and in various hospitals. They are standard however, at Veterans Administration Hospitals in the United States. Scales are: first year $4,205; second year, $4,990; third year, $5,365; fourth year, $6,440; fifth year, $7,405.

3 In the spring of 1965 interns and residents at Los Angeles County General Hospital staged a "heal-in," drawing attention to low pay by admitting every patient they could conceivably admit and keeping in hospital beds every patient who conceivably could be kept. During the first week of the heal-in the population of the 3,000 bed hospital hit 2,991.

In 1964 interns were paid $300 per month at Los Angeles County General Hospital. First year residents received $419 per month. An economic survey quoted by the young doctors in 1961 concluded that a man with a wife and two children needed $564 per month to live on, and the President of the Interns and Residents Association said that as of 1965, 80 percent of these residents and interns were "moon-lighting."

4 The American Hospital Association reported in 1963 that 781 hospitals maintained internship programs, and 1,240 hospitals maintained residency programs, that were approved by the American Medical Association.

Chapter Seven

1 Technical advances include the increase in numbers of medical schools, and concurrent increase in supply of interns and resident physicians for more community hospitals, the increase in "team medical techniques" which involved highly-trained personnel at every level, from doctor to equipment technician.

2 Dr. Buhler was addressing the annual meeting of the American College of Pathologists at Chicago.

Chapter Eight

1 In a mail survey conducted by the author in 1965 more than 100 hospital administrators cited the nursing shortage as either the most important or second most important problem facing them.

2 Nurses' pay varied widely around the United States in the 1960's, and even the status of nurses varied almost as widely. In some areas, such as Connecticut, there was a determined drive by the state nurse's association to secure legislation that would make the association a bargaining agent with hospitals and other employers. The drive failed in 1965 but was to be pressed again at the next session of the legislature.

   Nurses' pay rates for Connecticut in 1965 were: staff, general duty: $4,472-$5,598; Team leaders $4,680-$5,760; Assistant head nurse $4,929-$6,156; Head Nurse with RN status only $5,040-$6,760; head nurse with bachelor's degree $5,668-$7,150.

3 This was much like the Assistant Medical Officer plan mentioned below, as practiced in various Pacific Islands and the USSR and Iran.

Chapter Nine

1 Hospital wage rates varied widely in 1965, but in many areas they fell below the minimum wage rate of $1.25 per hour. Bureau of Labor Statistics showed the following spreads for nonprofessional hospital workers:

Memphis	$ .69 to	$ .84	per hour
Atlanta	.62 to	.84	per hour
Dallas	.84 to	1.05	per hour
Philadelphia	.90 to	1.10	per hour
Baltimore	1.10 to	1.20	per hour
Cincinnati	1.17 to	1.28	per hour
New York City		1.65	per hour

2 The total number of personnel employed by American hospitals in
1965 was 1,886,839, according to the American Hospital Association.
Of these, roughly 200,000 were employed in white-collar or administrative jobs, about 200,000 were employed in the dietary departments
of hospitals, and about 250,000 were employed in the household or
property departments, with 150,000 lumped under a category of "other
employees." This does not include the total of about 1,075,000 persons
engaged in the professional care of patients, doctors and those in nursing. The number of persons eligible for the concept "hospital labor,"
then, comes to about 600,000 or 800,000, depending on whether or not
one includes the administrative workers.

Outside the big cities with multiple hospitals, the potential membership for hospital unions is small and scattered, which accounts for the
slowness and reluctance of organized labor to move into this field.

3 One hospital administrator in New Hampshire told the author that he
fully expected a hospital union to begin activity in his hospital by
1970.

Chapter Ten

1 Medically indigent persons are not necessarily welfare cases, as Dr.
Albert Snoke of Yale-New Haven Hospital said to the author. The
"medically indigent" include those who pay their own way, but cannot afford medical or hospital expense of any kind.

2 Here are three cases involving open heart surgery at Yale-New Haven
Hospital in 1965.

Case No. 1: The patient was a teen-age boy, brought to this country
by an uncle, who personally had no insurance coverage and no personal funds; the cost of his care will presumably be paid by his
uncle, or persons of the same national background who might contribute toward the cost of his care.

Total Cost of Care—$2,661.97

Case No. 2: A private patient, with group insurance which is expected
to pay substantial benefits. (This patient may have remained in the
hospital longer than most open-heart patients, with continuous private duty nurses in attendance, as a result of the insurance coverage,
hence the size of the bill.)

Total Cost of Care—$6,161.09

Case No. 3: A teen-age girl whose open-heart surgery was completely paid for by the Aid to Dependent Children program of the state Welfare Department.

Total Cost of Care—$4,136.40

3 World Health Organization figures show that this is actually very low as compared to western Europe. Finland's rate was 27.6 per 100,000 people, for an unexplained reason; Venezuela's was only 5.1 per 100,-000.

4 Denmark's increase was 85%; England and Wales' rate was 30%.

Chapter Eleven

1 Result of author's survey of hospitals, plus complaints to the Secretary of Health, Education, and Welfare, reported in February and March, 1965. The NAACP complained that 41 southern hospitals were discriminating against Negroes. The report said: "This discrimination takes the form of segregation of Negro patients and staff members from white patients and staff members in rooms, wards, rest rooms, waiting rooms, cafeterias, and other facilities; provision of inferior facilities for Negroes using hospital services, and attempts by hospital personnel to dissuade Negroes from requesting or using desegregated facilities."

Chapter Thirteen

1 Writing in Hospital Topics in November, 1965, Philip M. Boffey of the Chicago *Daily News* reported Dr. Danielson's plans to cut costs to patients thus: "Establish a range of facilities for patients who don't need (and therefore shouldn't pay for) the usual nursing services. At Evanston Hospital use of the convalescent unit cut hospital bills in half. Patients who need only tests or minimal care are put in "hotel facilities that chop up to $13 off the daily room bill.

"—Reduce wasted time in the hospital by better scheduling of admissions and discharges; and eliminate unnecessary duplication of paper work.

"—Operate laboratories, X-ray units, operating rooms, radiation therapy units, and other facilities at night and on weekends if there is a demand. This would help avoid both wasted time and the need for expanding facilities.

"—Eliminate expensive duplication by sharing such facilities as laboratories, radiological services, emergency rooms, outpatient clinics, computers, and perhaps maternity units. Also share the services of such specialists as radiation therapists, physical therapists, biochemists, microbiologists, and many others.

"—Avoid establishing expensive units for cardiac surgery, neurosurgery, kidney dialysis, and radiation therapy unless there is a clear need. A survey at Johns Hopkins University revealed that 11 percent of the open-heart surgical facilities in the country performed not a single operation during 1961, while three-fourths of the remainder reported fewer than 50 surgical procedures, the minimum considered necessary to retain skill.

"—Close uneconomic hospitals. The executive director of the Hospital Planning Council for Metropolitan Chicago estimates that 15 percent of the 199 hospitals in the area are "borderline operations" that should either shut down or renovate extensively.

"—Halt unnecessary hospital construction.

"—Purchase more supplies jointly. The Chicago Hospital Council saved its members about $60,000 last year through cooperative buying of X-ray film, light bulbs, and other supplies.

"—Cut emergency-room costs by eliminating non-emergency cases. Evanston Hospital found that 37 percent of its "emergencies" were routine problems. The patients came to the emergency room because it was convenient for them or their doctors. The hospital now rents offices to physicians to handle these cases.

"—Use more automation, including Auto Analyzers in laboratories, automatic drug dispensers in pharmacies, automatic elevators and conveyor belts to move supplies, data-processing machines and computers to keep medical records, and educational television for teaching programs. Automation cuts the need for expensive personnel. One Auto Analyzer can do the work of two $450-a-month technicians."

2 In Michigan, Mississippi, Missouri, Montana, Maine—almost everywhere the states failed to pay the hospitals their stated costs of daily care of patients in compensation for care of welfare cases. Some states, such as Mississippi, paid $6.00 per day when the stated average hospital cost in that state was $22 per day.

Chapter Fifteen

1 Writing in *Medical World News,* December 17, 1965, Michael O'Neill, the magazine's Washington bureau chief reported: "Relevant to all

this is the fact that U.S. government health planners feel that some kind of AMO could help solve a lot of critical medical problems in this country. Such an 'assistant doctor' could perform many routine or relatively simple procedures under the supervision of fully trained physicians. AMOs could even be highly trained in certain limited functions, and perform these as well or better than an MD."

2 The Governor's Committee on Hospital Costs in New York State reported that hospital management in 1964 suffered badly in comparison with management of other industries, especially in use of manpower. Management consultants told the New York committee that they could cut 10 percent from the operating expenses of virtually any hospital in America. (That would keep hospital costs from going up for one year only.)

3 Dr. Trussell in an extensive interview with the editors of U.S. News and World Report, published July 26, 1965.

4 Public Law 89-07 provided hospital insurance for the aged under Social Security, voluntary medical insurance, an expanded Kerr-Mills program of aid to the poor, and Social Security coverage for doctors; Public Law 89-73 authorizes new administration of aged care and five-year grants for community aged care projects; Public Law 89-4 provides for construction of health facilities in economically depressed areas; Public Law 89-156 provides appropriations for the Health Education and Welfare Department and the Department of Labor's related agencies; Public Law 89-199 is supplemental appropriations for the Health, Education, and Welfare Department and the Department of Labor; Public Law 89-109 liberalized the immunization assistance program to localities, and gave the Public Health Service authority to designate diseases as public health menaces; Public Law 89-74 established controls for certain drugs with a potential for abuse; Public Law 89-291 provided for grants to assist in meeting needs for medical libraries; Public Law 89-290 gave federal operating funds for medical schools, scholarships for students, student loans, and increased medical school construction aid from the federal government; Public Law 89-105 authorized federal funds to help staff community mental-health centers; Public Law 89-234 provided for air-pollution control; Public Law 89-239 established regional medical complexes for research in the fields of heart, cancer and stroke; Public Law 89-115 gave funds for construction of health-research facilities and for additional assistant secretaries in the Department of Health, Education, and Welfare; Public Law 89-92 regulated labeling of cigarettes but barred curbs on cigarette advertising for three years.

5 Dr. Cutting spoke before the American Association for the Advance-

ment of Science. He also suggested that in a decade team medicine or group medicine would almost totally replace individual practice, and that nearly all medical services would be paid for through government or welfare funds.